# Two's Up

## A series of short stories about life in an ambulance

### By

# Buntie and Daffers

ISBN 978-1-80031-449-8


**www.newgeneration-publishing.com**

 New Generation Publishing

## <u>Dedication</u>

To our children
Kate, David, Zoe and Michael, you are our world

And all of our patients, who without you this book
wouldn't exist

**xxx**

# **Contents**

# Introduction

## Adult Content

Thank you for buying this book. We're assuming you're curious about what we get up to, so sit back and find out.

For the purposes of confidentiality some details have been changed, no real names are used, we don't mention areas etc for fear of identification and the ensuing court cases that would follow!

All the stories are true, it's also a reflection of how we feel, what makes us tick. The stories are based on our opinions only and not the ambulance service; no patients were hurt or ridiculed in the making of this book.

We are human and we share with you our human side; you really couldn't make it up!

## Who are we?

We are Sally and Marie, AKA Buntie and Daffers; our names came from having a particularly bad day at work and we often tease one another to cheer each other up. We do posh accents and one day Sally happened to say "oh come on, Buntie!" In her posh accent, I replied "Oh do come on, Daffers!" and it has simply stuck, so much so that we call each other by the aforementioned names on a daily basis, in fact I cannot remember the last time I called her Sally!

# Sally's story

I'm Sally, AKA Daffers. I've worked for the ambulance service for over sixteen years, before that I worked for a local water company as the first female in Leicestershire to be a distributions inspector. I'm no stranger to a challenge. But that's a whole different book!

I'm in my sixties now so, I've experienced a lot of what life can throw at you, I've loved and lost, raised my two lovely children, David and Kate, mostly alone, made some mistakes along the way but have learnt from them and managed to survive and I'm enjoying this stage of my life. I hope you enjoy the stories.

# Marie's story

I'm Marie, AKA Buntie. I have worked for the NHS on and off since I was nineteen years old and I am now fifty years old. I started Nursing and worked on wards and Accident and Emergency then settled in Emergency Assessment Units. Along the way I have had many jobs but all to do with human anatomy. I joined the Ambulance service trust around four years ago and have worked with Daffers for nearly two years now.

I'm a mum and a grandma and family are my everything. I'm also a widow and have been through the mill in my personal life, so working with Daffers has been my saviour.

# Buntie and Daffers

Greetings you lovely people, we are Buntie and Daffers! We work together on an Emergency Ambulance and hope to make a difference to people's lives when they need help and emergency treatment. We have worked together as a permanent crew for almost two years but before that we worked with many other crew mates. We realised that after working together previously that we had many things in common, including being mums having grandchildren, past relationship experiences and a similar outlook on life. We also have similar tastes and we view society and our community in the same way. We are two people that put our patients' needs first, we bring humour, empathy and compassion to the table and try to get the best result for everyone. We have a very childlike sense of humour which often results in the giggles and that helps us keep going!

## Never say too old

It was a Saturday night shift, I was working with a male colleague Steve who was slim, fit, athletic; most of which at 55+ years I wasn't. We were called to a young female in distress in a park, circumstances unknown. We arrived at the park to find the gates closed and locked. So, Steve did no more than climb up and over the locked gates with very little effort – obviously this must have been how the kids got in – leaving me on my own on the wrong side.

'Hang on' I said.

'Come on Sal, climb over.'

'I can't.'

'Yes, you can, just do it. This kid needs us.'

'OK.' So I started to climb, all went well until I got to the top. The gates were very ornate with spikes at the top, obviously to discourage and keep folk out, as well as looking in keeping with the ornate metal work. Feeling somewhat proud of myself for this achievement I started to descend. I hadn't realised that my trousers had got hooked on one of the spikes. I got part way down and decided to jump the rest of the way. The sound of the ripping was quite impressive; the gaping rip all the way up my trouser leg wasn't!

## Fart Gate

Gas, it's a tricky subject, it can cause embarrassment but also much hilarity, think of some comedy films you may have watched, with Peter Sellers or the Goons etc, flatulence is never far away.

It was a summer's evening and someone had fallen. We attended and found our patient had broken their hip. We assessed the situation and agreed we needed a scoop to move the patient, now we also needed to enlist the help of bystanders (which is often the way) to help lift the patient onto our ambulance stretcher. So, with everything and everyone ready on my command I said, "1, 2, 3, lift", we all took the strain. Unfortunately, the strain was probably a little too much for one person, as at that very moment the loudest fart was released (Buntie to describe how crisp it was). Now, being professional at all times is obviously at the forefront of our minds, however, this was one of those occasions when no amount of stiff upper lip was going to stop

what happened next. There was abash
one wanting to look at anyone for fear o
wrong person. A voice from behind me sa
was a *You're Been Framed* moment", to v
collapsed into ructions of laughter while,
the patient in mid-air now. If you've never had an
episode of uncontrollable laughter, let me tell you it's
very difficult to do anything, let alone hold onto and
indeed support the weight of a person in mid-air. So
there we were suspended, Buntie had lost it, I wasn't
far behind, but we managed to get the patient onto the
stretcher in one piece. The patient due to their hearing
impairment was oblivious to why we were all
laughing, lots of reassurance and explanations later all
was well, the patient made a full recovery, the identity
of the phantom raspberry blower will never been
known.


## A bit of how's ya father

Now, we are often called upon to assist patients to
mobilise, usually from sitting to standing or off the
floor so as to move them to our carry chair. This can
be quite challenging for some patients who are afraid
of falling or just don't have the energy to do it on their
own so, we assist as best we can. This means getting
very close, holding and supporting them; it's at this
point that the more nervous of our patients want to
hang on to us. Noy a problem normally but we're not
stupid, we know when a grip is really a grope!

It's not unusual to have a well-aimed hand placed
firmly on one's buttocks. So as not to offend we say
nothing at first, giving them the benefit of the doubt

, there's the odd occasion when the statement of please take your hand off my bum" just has to be said.

Sometimes it's heard and sometimes it's ignored. Take George (not his real name), he was a sauce pot, every time I moved his hand he'd put it straight back so, as his finger nails were quite long and sharp I had to really tell him off, "now look here, pack it in" in a loud voice so as the excuse of "oh, I can't hear you" won't be used. He gave me a big toothy grin, winked and said "I enjoyed that".

## Oops, I did it again

Driving is a big part of our job and sometimes we have some challenging obstacles to overcome. It's probably fair to say that in an ambulance career, if we've not had a bump or scrape, well, you're lucky!

It's 3 a.m. a patient needs help, the report was patient outside unconscious, every minute counted, I'm driving and Buntie is attending, she's readying herself to leap into action, we pull up to the address, there's a long gravel drive, flanked by two very sturdy looking oak posts. There were no street lights; with our spot lights on the ambulance, we could see a collection of people standing around a person lying on the ground. I parked the ambulance at the bottom of the drive and we dashed towards the patient to see what was the problem. The patient was a little worse for wear after a jolly night out and hadn't made it to their house. It was a cold night so we needed to get a move on. Buntie stayed with the patient and I went back to the ambulance. On my return to the vehicle I spot a white Transit van parked on the drive. 'Aha,' I think, 'if that van can fit so can I!'

I manoeuvre the ambulance to reverse up the drive knowing that Buntie needed me there pronto, it's going to be close but I'm confident I could get through, inch by inch I start to reverse, there's an overhanging tree to my left which knocks my wing mirror closed now I have no vision on that side, no worries I'll make sure I'm as close as I can on my right,with just millimeters to spare, damn!, the remaining wing mirror was just at the wrong height and I had to admit defeat, I was just going to have to carry the kit to Buntie.

I started to pull forward when it became apparent that now I was in I couldn't get out. Had the posts moved? It's at this point I heard the sickening sound of pieces of the ambulance being everso gradually removed; my word, these oak posts were pretty sturdy things I can tell you! They managed to remove with great ease all of the black rubber covering running down the length of the ambulance, two side lights and a wheel arch, my turretts was off the scale, I still had a job to do so I parked back where I started, jumped out of the cab and was greated by a very kind gentleman who had gathered all the bit of debris, he handed them to me me saying "I think these are yours".

With the kit in hand and somewhat breathless I returned to Buntie who looked at me giggling. "Having fun?" she asked.

We scooped our patient up and carried them to the ambulance. The patient was unharmed and needed nothing more than to be warmed up and sleep the alcohol off. They made a full recovery and so did the ambulance. Did I get in trouble I hear you ask, you bet I did.

# My little Bobby

If any of you have ever had the need to call for an ambulance, you may have been asked to put away any pets in another room. Our next patient decided that this wasn't necessary as their dog wasn't a threat to anyone.

On our arrival the patient was seated on the settee with a little Chihuahua dog sat next to them. The dog just looked as us with not much interest.

"Oh," I said, "how sweet."

"Yes, that's my little Bobby, he won't bother you."

With that reassurance I stepped forward towards the patient to be able to take some obversations, blood pressure etc, but stopped pretty sharpish when I heard the growling and saw the teeth. Not the patient, I hasten to add, but sweet little Bobby. Bobby had stepped forward to the edge of the settee and was letting me know that I wasn't welcome near his beloved owner. With a quick swipe of their hand, the patient tapped Bobby firmly on the side to which Bobby retreated to his basket.

"Sorry about that, he won't bother you again," said the patient, so I nerviously continued with one eye on Bobby who had indeed settled down and appeared to go to sleep in his basket.

After a short while it was decided that the patient needed further assessment in hospital so we set about organising ourselves, and as the patient wasn't mobile we needed to use our carry chair. It's a metal fold up chair with no arms and two wheels at the back that we use to move a patient from their property to the ambulance. When a patient is seated on the chair, we tip it slightly back and than we're able to push them forward. It's extremely important that whoever is supporting the back of the chair doesn't let go as the chair may tip backwards and the patient could be injured, so with the patient now on the chair and me supporting the back we proceded to move towards the front door. It's at this moment that sweet little Bobby woke up! Seeing his beloved owner being wheeled away by strangers, he decided it was time to leap into protective mode.

I first became aware of Bobby's intentions when I felt a sharp pain in my left calf as he sank his teeth into my leg. As I was in charge of the chair and was supporting the full weight of the patient, I couldn't let go. I let out a cry, I said something along the lines of "Oh dear, I think he's got me?" My crew mate hadn't seen Bobby's attack as she was bent over at the front of the chair waiting to lift the patient over the door step. On hearing my cry, she stood up but was unable to help as there was no room for her to get past the chair in the narrow hallway.

So, I was now trying to shake off Bobby who was vigorously biting at my trouser leg. I didn't want to alarm the patient by hurting Bobby but no amount of pushing Bobby away with my leg was having any affect. Balancing on one leg, with one last big flick I launched Bobby across through the doorway to the lounge across the room and fortunately he landed on the settee. This gave us just enough time to get over the front door step and close the door behind us before Bobby could mount another attack. The last thing we heard as we moved toward the ambulance was Bobby hurling himself at the now closed door. Fortunately the patient didn't notice as my crewmate skilfully distracted them with conversation. No patients or animals where hurt in the making of this story. This paramedic however still has the scars as a reminder of sweet little Bobby!

## What about your dog?

After Buntie and I started working together we realised that we had a lot in common; similar tastes and life experiences but also that we saw and felt the same things, like a sixth sense, instincts and gut feelings that other people didn't appear to pick up on. It was one of those occasions we'd like to share with you.

Buntie and I were with a patient that needed us to take to hospital. It wasn't a time critical transfer so we didn't have to rush to get things ready. It's common when we're in people's homes to notice things like photographs of family, hobbies, gardens etc. Also, we have to make sure that any other family members or pets are safe and secure once we've left the property. Now this person lived alone so there was just the dog to worry about.

As our patient gathered their toiletries etc together, I asked "Will someone be coming in to feed your dog?"

They replied "What dog?".

"The one in the hall I just saw."

"Yes," said Buntie, "he was there just a minute ago."

The patient looked at us in bemusement. "I haven't had a dog for over five years."

Buntie and I looked at each other and both asked "Was it a black dog?"

"Yes," came the reply.

"How did you know? He used to sleep on his bed in the hall."

# Larry the Lamb

Sometimes we come across the strangest of situations. It was a dark stormy night; I was working on my own in a FRV (Fast Response Vehicle). They are only for the highest priority jobs; we get sent first to assess and ascertain what else is required if anything.

It was late at night and I was returning to my base station after attending a patient, the route took me on the back roads across country. As I drove around a sharp bend I was confronted by several people running around, shouting and waving their arms. Just ahead of them were a two or three lambs and what I assumed to be their mother running around in a complete panic.

It quickly became apparent to me that the people running around weren't having much luck rounding the sheep up, as I drew level with one of the people I wound my window down and offered my services, something had to be done, knowing how fast some people drove on that stretch of road it was only a matter of time before an accident was going to happen, so, I drove past the nervous sheep, positioned myself just in front of them , put my blue lights on to warn other drivers of the hazard and slowly started to reverse back towards the sheep, they began to move as a group down the road toward the waiting farmers who had formed a cordon and now they were able to coral mum and lambs into a gated garden, job done!

After lots of thanks from the shepherds, I continued with my journey with a very satisfied feeling, knowing that with my help this situation had a happy ending. Which reminds me, I must get the lamb out of the freezer for tomorrow night dinner.

# Projectile pie

A patient required transferring from one hospital to another across town following an angiogram (a procedure wereby a tube is inserted into the femoral artery in the groin, a dye is passed into the tube and it goes to the heart where an X-ray can see if there are any blockages). When this procedure is done it's important the patient remains lying flat for some time afterwards to allow the wound to heal. All was going well; the patient was transferred to our ambulance, made comfortable and observations checked, so as I was the designated driver, on the instruction from my crew mate I jumped into the driver's seat and set off to the next hospital.

About five minutes into the journey I heard my crew mate shout, "Stop, he's going to be sick". Knowing that lying flat and vomiting are not a good combination I immediately pulled over and dashed to the back of the ambulance to assist. As I opened the back doors and stepped into the ambulance the first thing I remember seeing was my crew mate standing behind the patient waving frantically at me shouting, "Get out of the way". In the time it took me to compute, analyse and understand the situation the patient had let loose a large and very smelly quantity of vomit with such force towards where I was standing and was unable escape, the vomit hit me squarely in the face and dripped down my uniform into my pockets and down my cleavage. At this point my crewmate was stood frozen to the spot with an expression I can only describe as total disbelief and 'wait 'til I tell them about this on station'. The patient was looking somewhat relieved. I knew this because they then said "That's better, it must have been the cottage pie I had". It took me quite a while to pick the pieces of minced beef out of my pockets and cleavage. I continued the journey sitting on an incontinence sheet.

This happened about twelve years ago and to this day, my then-crewmate talks about it with great glee.

## This army marches on tea

Buntie and I love a cuppa, it's what keeps us going. On this occasion the family that we were with had very kindly made us a cup of tea. We had been on scene for a while sorting GP visits, district nurses etc. Sometimes it can take a while so as we waited for the GP to call back a second cup of tea was offered. Feeling slightly guilty I offered to make the next cuppa, so to the kitchen I went. Kettle on, cups at the ready, teabags, milk, sugar, all where you'd expect to find them. Now Buntie likes her tea strong and sweet so I dutifully let the teabag brew just a little longer, with of course two sugars. I knew she'd appreciate the extra effort.

"Tea up!" I shouted from the kitchen. Buntie gleefully entered the kitchen and drank her tea as did I. Immediately we both spat the tea out in unison. OMG who puts salt in the sugar caddy?

## A Woman

Some years ago, I was working with a male colleague, and we attended an elderly gentleman. Some of the oldest of the older generation often refer to us as either doctors for the men and nurses for the women. This gentleman was well into his nineties and my male crew mate was talking to him and the patient kept referring to him as 'Doctor' to which my colleague corrected him explaining that he was a technician and I was the paramedic to which the patient turned and looked at me for some time then said "they let women be paramedics, well I never". I smiled and explained that there's quite a lot of women on the service these days.

The gentleman required some further treatment at the hospital, so we set about getting ourselves and the patient organised. Once he was settled on the ambulance, I stepped off and climbed into the driver's seat as it was my turn to do so, to which I heard the patient say in a loud voice, "Good god, she's not driving as well?"

## Vim and Bleach

When I was a child, I remember that it was customary to clean the toilet with a combination of Vim and Bleach. This concoction would spit and fizz when combined but was a very effective way of getting the limescale off the toilet basin, as there were no modern limescale remover solutions available as there are today.

However, what we probably didn't appreciate was that by combining these agents we were unwittingly creating a volatile and explosive substance. When left alone this wasn't a problem and would be innocently flushed away, gleaming toilet intact.

Now I'm talking about the fifties and sixties, when it was common for people to smoke, especially the men folk who would retreat to the toilet fag in hand, newspaper under arm and spend some quite time doing their ablutions. When finished, the fag end would be innocently dropped down the toilet before being flushed.

It was one of these occasions when a gentleman did just that, unaware of the peril beneath. The explosion blew him off the toilet burning his backside and everything in that region.

An ambulance was called and again in those days there were no fancy stretcher trolleys with electrics, it was a simple fabric stretcher with two poles and patients had to be carried, so the patient now lying face down was telling his story of woe to the ambulance men (as it was predominantly men in those days), they were laughing so hard that they actually dropped the patient off the stretcher. The poor patient not only had a burnt bum and scorched testicles, but now a broken arm!

## Sorry

It was a hot summer's day, Buntie was driving and we had blue lights and sirens going. We were on our way to another emergency, it was rush hour in the city, and Buntie had her work cut out weaving in and out of the traffic.

Buntie often liked to chew gum which she was doing on this occasion, she suddenly started to cough and the chewing gum had gone down the wrong way, because she was driving at speed through the traffic she wasn't in a position to take her hands off the steering wheel, so, to deal with the problem and the offending item, she gave an almighty cough which brought the gum back up, as quick as a flash as we slowed for traffic she spat the gum out of the window, unfortunately just at that moment she had drawn alongside a car with its windows open waiting at the lights

The gum having now been expelled at pace was on a trajectory that couldn't be stopped. It hit the passenger of the other car on the side of the face and stuck there. Before words could be exchanged, the lights changed, the traffic moved and we were able to drive away pretty sharpish.

## He's my Hero

I was working with a male colleague who was young, tall, blue-eyed and rather dashing if I may say so. A real gent, he was eager to please and helped carry our equipment to and from the patients' houses. We had arrived at a male's house (I'd use the word *gentleman's*, but he wasn't), to find him sat on the bottom step of his stairs. It was evident quite quickly that he'd been drinking and was intoxicated. The story was that he had chest pain and had called 999 for assisstance. I entered first with my colleague close behind. I stood in front of the patient and after introducing ourselves asked how we could help, to which the patient looked at my chest and said "I need some titty to make me better". Now, I'm no shrinking violet and have no problem advising a person of the error of his waysso. I was just about to advise said patient of his mistake when I was aware that I was moving, two strong arms had literally picked me up and moved me 180 degrees around, my male colleague was now standing in front of the patient and let's say telling him in no uncertain terms that his behaviour was and if there was any more of it he'd be sorry and he was to appologise to me, oh swoon!

The patient did appologise and we looked after him accordingly. He hadn't had a heart attack but did have a chest infection. He was very quiet throughout the observations, especially as my colleague was just a few feet away and hadn't taken his eyes off him for a second.

I later thanked my crew mate for chivalrous conduct. No matter how tough you think you are, it's nice to go back to when the men folk looked after their ladies.

## The Black Dog

The Black Dog is something we in the emergency services refer to as the symbol of mental health, depression, predominately for ourselves, it's the gradual creeping up of things that are stored in our inner selves, all the anger, all the strife, the horrible things we see, hear, feel. It's not a case of if, but when these things will materialise and manifest into something not ourselves. That's when the Black Dog descends. He's huge and overwhelms us, he takes over our entire world; we can't function, we descend into a world of despair. Everything becomes a struggle, getting out of bed, eating, going to the bathroom, this is depression at its worst.

Sadly, there have been some suicides. One is too many. My personal experience is five of my colleagues have taken their own lives. Something had to be done.

Today, with the enormous work and support of staff across the board in the ambulance service, a peer-to-peer support network was set up, dedicated to the staff from every level. We are today much more aware of our own vulnerabilities and can recognise an individual that seems to be struggling.

We also work closely with other outside agencies who can support staff when needed just as I did in 2017, when I had my own Black Dog experience and my world came crashing down. Until you've experienced it you can't possibly comprehend how difficult it is to 'pull yourself together'. If only it was that simple.

## When things don't go according to plan

Working in the ambulance service is probably one of the best jobs in the world and for me it's exactly that. No two days are the same, we see the worst and the best of life and are privileged to be asked in to strangers' homes who are putting all of their faith in you to do the right thing.

But not all situations go according to plan. I was working a nightshift; a call came in to 'back up' a paramedic who was on scene on his own with a young woman who was having a miscarriage. We set off at pace, knowing that this was going to be difficult for us all.

On arrival the paramedic was kneeling on the floor at the top of the stairs. Now, who are we to say how people should live, but to say this house was a dump is a slight understatement. There were no carpets, just one light bulb in the hall; it looked like someone had smeared mud up the walls that hadn't been decorated in many years. Our boots stuck to dirt on the floor, there were several teenage boys wandering around and a dog, a staffie to be precise, so, seeing the paramedic on his knees I thought this must be serious for him to even attempt to kneel in the dirty conditions.

The woman – or girl as she was only fifteen years old – had indeed miscarried at thirteen weeks of pregnancy. John the paramedic told us she'd fainted and the foetus had come away all intact. When this happens, apart from the patient going to hospital, the foetus and anything else that comes away must go too so as the doctors can assess if any surgery is required. With this in mind I asked John where was everything. He replied 'I put it all in a bowl, behind me'.

'Where?' I asked again?

'Over there,' he pointed frustratedly.

'No, sorry the bowl's empty!'

We all looked down the stairs to just see a tail disappear around the corner. 'Someone stop that dog!'

After much rushing around from us the foetus was recovered and on inspection no damage had been done. We apologised profusely but honestly no one seemed the slightest bit bothered, except the ambulance crew.

The girl was taken to hospital and reports submitted for safeguarding as she was underage and regarding the living conditions. By the way, there were no adults at this property either.

# Are we moving?

When I look back to my earlier career, I see how green I was, how inexperienced and naïve but aren't we all when the subject matter is new to us? It was not long after I'd started and getting used to so many aspects of the job, not just patients, but equipment, driving, hospitals and much more.

Another night shift, call to an RTC (road traffic collision), we arrive. The car was parked on a tree, the tree appeared to have won. The three occupants of the car had all decamped and were walking around in a daze with various minor cuts and bruises. Shortly after our arrival the police arrived, so the worst of the patients who said had some abdominal pain was shown to the stretcher while the other two took seats. Two police officers and us all climbed onto the ambulance, making seven people in total. It was cosy!

A few months earlier our fleet of very tired ambulances had been updated and we were one of the first crews to get a nice new shiny one. Everything appeared to be the same except for the handbrake, which was now on the right. No big deal. I'll remember eventually after I've thumped my hand about a dozen times on the box where the handbrake used to be.

What the manufacturer had forgotten to tell us was that the new braking system had a fault; as the brakes cooled down the handbrake loosened off, and as you can imagine after we've been thrashing the life out of the vehicle to get to patients, it gets pretty hot. So, if you haven't left the vehicle in gear then if on a hill there was nothing to stop it from moving. Add in a bit of extra weight, like seven people in the back, and you've got a very scary situation.

On this occasion the collision was on a country road which ran parallel with a quarry and the roads were mostly on a slope. I'd parked the ambulance facing downwards towards the quarry where the car was. We were all in the back of the ambulance when one of the police officers said, 'Are we moving?' Sure enough, there was just the slightest of groans from the vehicle as the handbrake started to release. Realising what was happening I jumped off the vehicle, dashed around the side and ran to the driver's door. The ambulance was now beginning to move toward the quarry. To this day I don't know how I managed it but I opened the door climbed in and thrust my foot on the brake. It took me several minutes to stop shaking just at the sheer thought of what could have happened. To this day I always leave any vehicle in gear, phew!

## Patience is a virtue

Dementia, in my opinion, is probably one of the cruellest diseases ever. People locked in a perpetual state of forgetfulness, anxiety, zombified while the poor family have to look on helpless to do anything. As a paramedic I work very hard to make any of my needed interventions as gentle as can be, with the aim to not take any patients with dementia or Alzheimer's to hospital but occasionally this can't be helped. It was one of those occasions and not as grim as you may think; in fact, quite the opposite.

We had been called to a residential home to see Mary (not her real name). Mary had fallen and had fractured her wrist, so a trip to hospital couldn't be avoided. Mary was a real delight, happy and pleasant, she loved everyone. We settled her onto the ambulance making sure she was as comfortable as possible. My role, after pain relief, was to just talk to her. This is where it gets challenging.

Mary's memory had a life span less than a goldfish so she would ask you a question, immediately forget what you've said, then ask the same question again followed by, 'Oh, you are lovely'. The journey was approximately twenty-five minutes to the nearest hospital; the family had agreed to meet us there so it was just me and Mary. She asked me where were we going.

'To the hospital,' I replied.

'Oh, that's nice, oh you are lovely.'

Two seconds later. 'Where are we going?'

'To the hospital, Mary.'

'Why's that then?'

'You've broken your wrist.'

'Have I?'

'No, no, Mary, don't move it.'

Silence.

'Where are we going?'

'To the hospital' and so on and so on. It was the longest twenty-five minutes of my life but I never stopped answering her and she never stopped asking. We held hands, just mostly to stop her from waving her hands around.

Her parting words were the funniest. As my male colleague came on board once we arrived, Mary looked him up and down and said 'Oh, he's a bit of alright, I could do something with him.' I don't know who went redder, him or me from laughing.

# Mummy and Daddy are away!

I remember when I was a teenager, I'd have loved my mum and dad to have gone away: the whole house to myself, music on full blast, jumping on the bed, eating jam sandwiches for tea in front of the TV but no such luck. Unlike my next two patients, who weren't just jumping on the bed but having sex on it!

We arrived to hear screaming, I mean ear-piercing screaming, the doors and windows were shut so just how loud could this girl be, the front door was unlocked so we went straight in and could tell the sound was coming from upstairs, we dash up calling out who we were as we went, a voice shouted come quick, she's bleeding.

As we entered the bedroom, there were two young people in their underwear. She was sitting on the bed with blood all over her legs and stomach; he was standing, holding his penis with a towel and screaming, 'She's bleeding, she's bleeding'. It quickly became apparent to us that it was in fact the lad that was bleeding.

The parents had gone away for the weekend; their daughter, a sixteen-year-old, was staying with her friend, but the daughter felt this was an ideal opportunity to invite her boyfriend over and have sex in the comfort of Mummy and Daddy's bed.

The boyfriend was also sixteen and it transpires that they were both virgins. In the heat of the moment the young man had got a little carried away and in his haste and vigour had split his foreskin, which for any males reading this knows that not only does it hurt like hell but it bleeds profusely, so I'm told.

In his panic the lad had run around the bedroom screaming and managed to spray blood everywhere: all over the bed, up the curtains, on the carpet. Mummy and Daddy are going to be mightily cheesed off when they returned home the next day however, paramedics to the rescue.

After, calming the lad down enough for us to stem the bleeding and educate him to that his old man won't drop off and he would be able to father children in the future, we agreed we'd help the kids clear up. It took us maybe thirty minutes to strip the bed, clean the carpet, take the curtains down (which luckily were machine washable) and wash the walls, phew!

By the time we'd all finished you wouldn't have known anything had happened. I've never seen such grateful kids, big hugs all round and parting advise we left feeling like superheroes!


## Is he really dead?

Death is something we encounter unfortunately all too often in this job and it can be challenging to deal with on a personal level. People often ask how we cope; do we get used to it? Well, the short answer is no, you can't really because the Grim Reaper takes us in so many different ways and when you get that call, you don't know what you're going to be faced with.

I think it's fair to say that there's a pocket of the population however that are determined to meet their maker much earlier than is required. Take Clive (not his real name). Clive was one of life's more challenging characters; he passed most of his time drinking and when he wasn't drunk, he was asleep and that was it. He had a close network of friends who would periodically bring him food and of course, more drink.

Clive's main hobby was to call 999 from a telephone box that was just outside his house, stating he had chest pain. We would attend and do an assessment knowing we'd not find anything, reassure him, then leave. This would happen three to four times a week at different times of the day. Why? I hear you say. We have to attend these situations as one day Clive might just be having a heart attack. As for his mental health and drinking, he was already well and truly in the system of care, however that only works if the patient engages with the system and Clive had long ago decided he wasn't going to, so this was the situation that meant we all went round in circles.

One day a call came in: 'cardiac arrest'. We immediately recognized the address: 'Clive'. Off we set, grumbling the whole way that Clive had gone too far this time and I was going to give him a piece of my mind, there could be some other poor soul out there needing us etc.

We arrive, the front door was open. As we walked in the first thing I noticed was the number of flies in the house, and sure enough laying on the settee, surrounded by bottles was Clive. Dead! We didn't start CPR (cardiac pulmonary resuscitation), as it was clear Clive had been dead for several days. We contacted the police as is the policy when it's an unexpected death at home. Clive was only in his thirties and his lifestyle somewhat chaotic, so we couldn't rule out foul play. While we were waiting for the police to arrive my colleague commented on how she thought his chest was moving. I stepped forward to take a closer look.

Indeed, his chest was moving ever so slightly and little bubbles were coming out of one of his nostrils. I leaned in closer, in my head I was certain he was dead as his skin had already started to turn a dark leathery colour, his eyes were sunken, he was dead.

At that moment a rather large fat bluebottle shot from his nostril at speed. I was now just inches away and clearly in the fly's way. It hit me smack between the eyes. I was so startled by this I shot backwards, stepped on an empty bottle which then turned me into a *Dancing on Ice* participant, spun me round and with my arms flailing like a wind mill, collided with the coffee table and was propelled sideways over the top and landed head first onto a very soiled armchair. Enter PC Plod. My crew mate had to leave the room as she was laughing so hard. I was struggling to extricate myself from the chair trying desperately not to disturb anything else. The policeman just stood in stony silence.

There was no foul play and Clive had simply drunk himself to death. It never ceases to amaze me that it's such a waste of life. Who knew why he was the way he was; only he knew and his poor mum who lived just around the corner and was going to get that dreaded knock on the door.

## How dare you?

The public often ask us if we get a lot of abuse. I wouldn't say a lot, but it does happen and not always from drunks and alike.

Meet Frank (not his real name). Frank had fallen in his flat. He lived alone and because of his poor mobility was unable to get himself up. His accommodation was assisted living in a complex of apartments, all fitted with emergency pull cords and lifelines. The lifeline had been activated by Frank and we were asked to attend to help.

On arrival we entered by the unlocked door to Frank's flat. We called out saying who we were and to hopefully get a reply, so we knew were the patient was. It was a reply we weren't expecting.

'Get me off this f…...king floor' came the response. Now I'm tolerant of a certain amount of poor behaviour in distressing circumstances but this was out of proportion for the situation. We walked around the corner to find Frank laying on his back on the kitchen floor. The conversation that followed proved to me and my colleague what a thoroughly unpleasant individual Frank was.

'Hello, Frank what happened?'

'Never mind all that crap, ya silly cow just f…..king get me up.'

'Frank, don't be so rude and stop swearing, we're here to help.'

Then 'f……king help, ya silly bitch.'

Right, that did it. I think I've lost my temper just twice on this job over fifteen years and this was one of those times. My crew mate was also trying to calm Frank and she too was getting verbally abused.

I stood up, looked at Frank, who by the way had no injuries and no pain, and shouted 'Your behaviour is disgusting. We've asked you to stop the abuse and still you persist. We will not tolerate this and if you continue we will leave, do you understand?'

Guess what the reply was? 'Then f…..k off.'

'Well, you need us more than we need you' and with that we left but, don't panic, folks, we had no intention of leaving Frank to struggle. We stepped outside just long enough for him to reflect.

After maybe five minutes, we went back in. 'Shall we try again, Frank?' He said nothing. We got him to his feet, escorted him to a comfy chair, made a cup of tea for him, checked all his vitals which were all good. In this time, Frank said nothing.

We packed our equipment away and were just going out through the door when a little voice said 'Sorry'.


## Don't take everything as gospel

The report came in that an elderly lady had fallen over the back door and was now lying outside. Our instructions were to gain access via the back gate. It was winter and the temperature hadn't gone much above freezing all day so time was of the essence.

When we arrived we headed for the back gate as instructed, only to find it locked. There was a gap between the gate and the post; it was locked too. I could see that the bolt was at the top. Being vertically challenged at 5'2" I was unable to reach over the top, so instructing my crewmate to hold her folded hands as a step I launched myself up, grabbed the top of the gate frame and… stop.

What I or my crew mate Kate couldn't see was the razor wire that had been placed along the top of the gate and fence. I had now got both my hands firmly impaled onto the wire. With much swearing and some grunting from Kate, as she still had my full weight on her hands, I managed to release myself and returned to ground level, both hands now bleeding and smarting like hell.

'Oh, hello, are you the ambulance crew here for Maud? She's in the lounge,' came the voice of a friend of Maud's.

We made our way now to the front door and into the lounge where indeed Maud was sitting with her two other friends who'd come round and picked Maud up off the ground, taken her indoors and made tea for all. I sat listening to all this while my hands bled. I asked Kate if she wouldn't mind getting some dressings.

'Oh, you won't need those,' said one of Maud's friends. 'She's not hurt herself.'

'It's for me,' I said as I showed them my bleeding, ripped hands.

'Oh, the wire,' said Maud. 'My son put that up the other week, it's so reassuring that it works!'

## I couldn't believe my eyes

We were called to an address in the city, on arrival we were greeted by a local doctor familiar with the patients and her history, he seemed somewhat agitated as we pulled up in our ambulance, 'quick you must get this lady out now before her son or family arrive!', 'why, who, what's going on, we asked' we entered the house we could see that the door had been forced open, two policemen stood in the hall, we were shown to a front room that had been converted into a bedroom for this lady.

What greeted us was by far one of the worst cases of neglect I've come across. The elderly lady was lying on top of the bed, her clothes dirty, the smell pungent, she had nothing on her legs or feet, I looked at her feet in disbelief completely mesmerised, unable to concentrate on what was being said around me, this patients toe nails were unbelievable they were so over grown they had grown about 2 inches forward then had gone sideways at a 90 degree angle possibly due to slippers, then they had continued on their journey encountering the next toe, no problem, just grow through it, success, they appeared on the other side of the toe, the flesh no obstacle, OMG but this wasn't the worst of it, when I finally looked away from the toes I could see her left arm was a strange shape, and it got worse.

The doctor gave us a resume of her injuries and the circumstances around them.

Elderly lady lives alone; numerous falls; fractures, none of which had been seen at hospital due to the fact that the family, primely the son, had kept everyone away. There had been concerns for this lady for a while and today it had all come to a head with police and us called.

It's at this moment the son arrived. He was immediately hostile: who had broken the door, who did we think we were, what the f...k was going on, we'd had no right to enter etc.

It quickly became clear why the doctor was so anxious to take the patient out of the property asap, because once the son was on scene the patient refused to cooperate.

'He'll look after me!' she said.

So now it was standoff; us and the doctor trying desperately to convince the patient she really needed help, while the son ranted about his mother's rights. He appeared to be well-informed, unfortunately!

After a lot of arguing the son was becoming more and more agitated, which actually played into our hands because the police could then step, in which they did, and the son was eventually arrested.

With the son out of the picture our patient appeared to have forgotten about him quite quickly, ah dementia in there I suspect, so we started again,' how'd you like to see a nice doctor and get those toenails sorted?

'OK, that would be nice,' came the reply.

This lady was in hospital for a number of weeks. I visited just the once to see how she was doing. She didn't remember me or indeed anything that had happened recently. Her dementia had very quickly taken her into her past and she was very happy talking to her husband who had been dead twenty years.

For me, it was nice to see what she looked like now that she was clean, fed and those hideous toenails gone.

Social services had been called and it was deemed 'unsuitable' for her to go home so she was moved to a nursing home where she lived for three years before she passed away.

## Years of training

Old wives' tales are just that, or are they?

We speak to many communities – Polish, Russian – but the Asian community always greets us with the most warmth. They usually want to feed and water us with cakes and chia tea (which is delicious). There's always lots of hugs. They're genuinely pleased to see us.

It's while working with this community over the years that I noticed a pattern emerge; without fail, when one of their loved ones was ill out would come the vapor rub, applied liberally to the chest, arms, legs, and neck indeed as many areas as possible.

Meet Ahmed (not his real name). His family had called us because he had had chest pain for a few hours and they were worried. We arrived with our defibrillator in hand so we could get an ECG reading to determine if Ahmed was having a heart attack.

I was immediately aware of the rather strong smell of vapor rub, and I had it confirmed when my ECG (electrocardiogram) stickers wouldn't stick to Ahmed's chest, that his mother had plastered vapor rub on. It was so bad that at one stage my eyes were streaming so much I couldn't see but by god, my sinuses were lovely and clear!

Another unlucky patient had lost a fight with a food mincer and the end of his finger had gone into the mix!

Years of training, but I needn't have worried, all I really needed was turmeric. This well-known spice has healing properties like no other, well it must have because this patient's now shorter digit was dipped in the stuff. Maybe they thought it would help it grow back? I appreciate the thought, but this patient wasn't too impressed when we had to wash the stuff off. He was very vocal in his own language. I think he said something like 'by 'eck, that smarts.'

So, to hell with my books on pharmacology and bags of drugs to carry, it's vapor rub and turmeric from now on.

Ps. Ahmed wasn't having a heart attack and the other patient's finger never grew back.

# Behave yourself

I was working on the FRV (Fast Response Vehicle) which means you work on your own; a call came in, 'cyclists RTC, multiple casualties'. The thought of multiple casualties filled me with dread but I needn't have worried.

When I arrived on scene, I was greeted by about six men, all kitted out as you would expect experienced cyclists to be. The story was that one group had been travelling downhill, while the other group had been travelling in the opposite direction. Unfortunately the downhill group had come to a sharp 90% bend and one had overshot the bend meaning they were now on the wrong side of the road and met the other group. Result: bent bikes and injured riders.

I quickly prioritised the injuries, which amounted to no more than cuts and bruises. Some needed cleaning and dressing. The gentlemen formed an orderly line and I worked my way through the injuries. One gentleman had grazes to his thigh and hip. Now we were all standing on the grass verge, so very much in the public gaze. I was about to suggest that he sit near my car as a screen but as quick as a flash he pulled his shorts down. Well, I didn't know where to look; it's not often these days that something makes me blush, but I had gone puce, much to the amusement of the other men.

# The code word

I was mentoring a student called Alex. He was in his second year so had some experience; it was 1 o'clock in the morning and we were called to a male, unconscious. Off we set. We talked about possible scenarios: fight, ill health, old, young etc and treatments we could give. When a new student comes to me I am acutely aware of their vulnerabilities and the situations they may face for the first time while working with the public. We never know what we will encounter so I always tell them, if we go to a job that is unsafe I will ask you to go (for their own safety) to the car and fetch a piece of equipment that doesn't exist, i.e. a DCB , which stands for 'don't come back'. You never think you're going to have to use this coding however.

We arrived at a block of bed sits in not a very affluent area. No lights were on. We entered cautiously, calling out who we were. In the hallway there were several doors leading to bedsits, the first door we came to was number 3, which seemed a little strange as what happened to number 1? Anyway, we knocked. A gruff, slurred male voice said, 'Ya, mate, it's open, come in'. The room consisted of a space about 10x10, squeezed into which was a single bed, one armchair, a sideboard and one room length of countertop with sink. The male was sat on the bed, the lighting was poor; just one small lamp in one corner, top light missing a bulb. In the armchair was another male, fast asleep.

'How can we help you?' I asked with my student next to me.

'It's 'im,' said the male on the bed pointing to the male asleep in the chair. 'He's doing mi 'ead in and I want you to get rid.'

At that moment, before I could reply, my student was nudging me in the side. 'Sal, Sal.' I turned to him and followed his gaze. Propped up on top of the sideboard was a hand gun. We'd walked right past it. A million things were going through my head not least *bugger, shit* and *how are we going to get out of this?* The code word!

Before I could give the code word however, our male sat on the bed, who we will call Tommy (not his real name), said 'Don't take no notice of that,' pointing at the gun. Then said 'But if ya don't get rid of this twat,' (pointing to the male still asleep in the armchair), 'I'll shoot 'im.' Ah, well, bugger, bugger, shit, shit, shit!

'Alex, would you mind getting the DCB for me?' Alex stared at me for what seemed an eternity his face serious and the colour had gone, with some hesitation he said he would, I still had my radio so I gave it to Alex and asked him to let control know that we would be a little while, and also telling Tommy that this was because control like to know how long we will be on each job, normal procedure, but Alex knew I meant for him to tell them that I was now with a man who had a hand gun! With my student out of harm's way I set about engaging Tommy in conversation. He invited me to sit on the bed with him and I did, not because I'm stupid but to pacify. I'd say Tommy was about 7 stones wet threw, probably due to his alcoholism, so felt pretty confident I could side-step him if he got silly. Everything was nice and calm; our armchair occupant still asleep; a sound at the door. Alex had returned! NO! Bugger, bugger, shit, shit, shit. If looks could kill, I'd just sent a stunner to Alex. He never flinched.

Plan B, all praise to Alex, he said he couldn't find the DCB and could I help him? Clever boy!

'Tommy, we'll be back in a minute.'

'Ya, no probs, darlin.'

With that we both left. When we left the property, the man and his world were in the street: police, firearms, the boss. WE were instructed to move to a meeting area further up the road.

The last we heard, Tommy was arrested for possession and threatening behaviour, meanwhile I believe his mate is still asleep in the armchair!

Alex was my hero, but I still chastised him for coming back. Lol x


## Domestic violence

'He's always sorry after and I do love him.' But is it always *he*?

This is a tricky subject and I thought long and hard whether to include this story but the story needs telling, if only to highlight the plight of women and men who suffer daily from physical abuse.

I was working solo on a FRV (fast response vehicle), it was about midnight a call came in, male with serious bleeding, that's all the information I had, it was the highest priority so I got a move on, speeding through the streets, I arrived to find a detached house in a well-to-do area, the front door was open and the lights were on, I could see very quickly that there was glass and blood in the hall, I entered cautiously, calling out to anyone who may have been there.

A voice from the kitchen, 'Hi, yes, it's me.' A man sitting on a chair in the kitchen holding a tea towel to the right of his neck. I could see lacerations to his arms, blood was everywhere, glass scattered.

'OK, so, who did this?' I asked. 'And where are they now?'

'Don't worry, they've gone.'

'Gone where?'

'Don't know.'

'So it's just you then?'

'Yes.'

'OK, let's have a look at you.'

He had cuts to his neck – just millimetres away from his jugular vein – done with a broken wine glass; cuts to his arms, defensive, and bruises to his face. As I patched him up I asked lots of questions about the events leading up to this. It was a familiar story: wife, husband, drink, fight, but it was the female in this scenario that appeared to be the perpetrator. I only had his side of the story.

What was really sad about this story is the victim was a retired policeman and the wife a nurse working in A&E. OMG, I couldn't get my head around this. Two people who have had to deal with domestic violence at its worst and are now embroiled in their own nightmare.

The answer is of course is alcohol, mixed in with emotional turmoil – the demon that destroys so much in this world.

## Cardiac Arrest

It's 6 o'clock in the morning, I've just logged on for my day shift when a call comes in: 'cardiac arrest, body found on driveway'. I jump into the car, and floor it, dashing through the traffic that is unusually heavy for 6 in the morning,

Now there are four categories of drivers on the roads that the ambulance service encounter: there's the 'we know what to do and pull over to the left, we go by, thank you,'; then there's 'we see you and don't know what to do and pull over to the right, we anticipate you,'; then there's the third 'we see you coming and haven't a clue what to do so slap the anchors on anywhere, usually with their eyes shut, we anticipate you and try not to park our half ton of ambulance up your exhaust, as it's way too much paperwork and the boss get really upset,; then the fourth and most irritating 'we see you and just keep going anyway'. What can I say? 'Arse holes'. I encounter all of these on this journey; all this while being updated by my control that the police have been dispatched, another crew and an EMICs Doctor and will meet you at the scene, no other details have been given as in age, gender etc so I plough on still impeded by sleepy drivers!

'Stand down, stand down' comes the voice over the radio from control, it's not a human body, it's a dead bird!, how? I hear you ask, apparently a bit of a language barrier.


## Pregnant dog

A call comes in , I'm working as a crew, the jobs came throw on our screen as, 'female pregnant in pain', we rush to the scene, the information is limited, 'A46, between this town and another', so, just the 5 miles to check then, we come off a roundabout junction and are about two miles in when we see a couple walking on the grass verge, surely not it's a dual carriageway not suitable for pedestrians , they have with them a dog. We pull up at the side of them with blue lights flashing to warn other drivers of the hazard.

"Have you called for an ambulance?"

"Yes," came the reply. "Our dog's pregnant and we've not got any money to get home and we're stuck on this carriageway."

Now god help me I'll help anyone but for god's sake really, what were they thinking, what did they think would happen when they embarked on their journey on the dual carriageway? It beggar's belief. I wonder if they would have called if they had to pay? Hmmm!

## I'm having a heart attack, help me!

It was a day shift and we were called to a male found by members of the public lying on a grass verge, on a busy road. When we arrived, a man of about 55-60 years old was lying on the grass clutching his chest. We took our stretcher to him so as not to walk him and moved him onto the ambulance, out of the view of the public.

"I'm having a heart attack," he said. "Help me."

"Don't worry, sir, we will help you." We did all the checks, everything seemed in order but he was complaining of 9 out 10 pain which is significant, so I gave him some GTN (glyceryl trinitrate) and an aspirin, as per protocol. However, when I offered him some morphine intravenously he declined, which I have to say confused me somewhat at the time, as he appeared to be in a lot of discomfort but, such is his right of choice, so, we transported him to the nearest hospital (which happened to be in the centre of town) for further investigations i.e. blood tests which we can't do and is the definitive test, when we arrived at the hospital we off loaded the patient from the ambulance and took him into hospital department. It was a busy time and the nurses were particularly stretched. Rather than wait for the nurse to come to me for hand over, I went to the nurses' station to save time. It was at this stage our patient found his opportunity and left!

Yes, folks, it was a massive scam. He legged it out of department to a waiting friend. I last saw him running down the road with his friend. I was furious. No wonder he didn't want any morphine – that would have really spoilt his night out. It appeared that we were the free lift into town! The human race never ceases to disappoint; just when I think I've heard and seen everything. What a horrible human being.

Each time an ambulance is dispatched and a patient is taken into hospital it costs over £2000. What a low life. I have many more words to describe this person and people like him who abuse our precious NHS, but I'm not allowed to print them!

## The brush handle up bottom

When it comes to language barriers it can really impede one's progress. Take the metal brush handle up one's rectum.

Yes, you read that correctly. I was working with a male colleague whose approach to life was somewhat 'relaxed'. A call came in 'amber back up', male, abdominal pain, we arrive and found a paramedic with a patient who was thrashing around on the bed, (not the paramedic) the paramedic scratching his head, saying, 'I don't know what the hell is going on here, he keeps pointing to his bum and crying in pain, I've tried to ask what, where, etc but no one here speaks English, I look around and the patient's wife is standing in the hall, looking very worried. I approach and gently ask, with the use of hand and body gestures, what's happened? She shows me a brush. OK. Then another brush identical to the first except, the second brush had part of its handle missing. Approximately 13 inches to be precise. Oh. She points to the broken brush then points to her husband still writhing around on the bed. Oh, oh dear, are you telling me that the missing part of this brush is in your husband? All done with pointing gestures. *Yes* came the nod. Holy shit, this is serious. Regardless as to how it happened, this is a medical emergency. I update my colleagues whose faces were just dumbstruck.

"OK, so as you guys are pretty much useless I'll make the calls," I said. I called our resuscitation team, and yes had to say it twice as they didn't believe what I was saying or suggesting. We moved the patient lying down to the ambulance, very carefully. This potentially could be a ruptured bowel, life-threatening so the utmost care was needed and that's what we did.

When we arrived at resus (resuscitation, the highest priority for patients), the team were waiting. I gave them a breakdown of what was the presenting problem. The wife accompanied us with the broken brush. We couldn't find anyone in the department who spoke the same language so it was still hand and body gestures.

The patient went to surgery and indeed had 13 inches of metal brush handle removed from his rectum and bowel with no lasting damage. To say he was lucky is an understatement and of course the jokes came flooding in. "Her Sal, hear putting a brush up my arse and sweeping as I go is OK with you." Very funny.

## Emotional distress

Emotional distress does strange things to people; sometimes they're quiet, sometimes they're violent. You can never tell what you're going to get, so you must be ready for anything.

Enter Leroy. Leroy was a three-month-old baby. I was working solo on the FRV (fast response vehicle), and was dispatched to him as he had some difficulty breathing. When I arrived I entered the front room of a terraced house. Mum, Dad, Auntie and little Leroy were present. Leroy was in his mother's arms. Clearly sniffly, I approached not touching baby, talking to the audience about what and how I could help, Leroy's dad then stepped forward and grabbed me by my shirt now, Leroy's dad was what we call in the trade as a large unit, not fat but well-built and muscular, he was distressed and obviously worried about his first born so with very little effort he lifted me off the floor by my shirt which in some way I was glad was robust enough to hold me, and said, "You do something to help my boy." I replied, "OK, well to do that I need you to put me back down and let me do my job" i.e. help Leroy. he did as I asked and lowered me to the ground, it's no exaggeration to say I was shaking like a leaf, but I never let on, I called for backup and to my relief, a crew arrived very quickly, all the time caring for little Leroy who had got a cold, and a blocked snotty nose, which I easily remedied with some repositioning and oxygen (which he didn't need, so it wasn't actually on but it kept Dad calm ), patient OK, paramedic completely buggered.

I later found out that Leroy's dad worked on the doors, hence the build, but no matter how hard or big you are, a baby in distress will floor you every time.

## Does my bum look big in this?

I arrived to find the neighbours round the back of the house, a ladder up against the wall. The story was that an elderly lady who lived in the house alone, had not been heard from for a couple of days. One of the neighbours had climbed up the ladder and seen Mrs Smith (not her real name) lying on the floor of her bedroom and had then called the ambulance service, so here I was.

Up the ladder I went. There was a small window open and as I was the smallest it was up to me to climb in. I could see the lady on the floor; she wasn't moving or responding to my calls. As is usual, a dressing table was under the window that I was struggling to climb through. As I pulled myself through like a slug I caught my trousers on the window latch. I could hear rude comments from the neighbours, who were laughing at my predicament. I was grappling with the problem and with one final tug my trousers released and I entered the room at pace, unfortunately all of Mrs Smith's lovely ornaments, perfume bottles and silver hairbrushes went for a burton. I was apologising profusely but this wasn't a priority as poor Mrs Smith had clearly had a stroke.

# It's so sad

I've added this story for a very good reason. I implore you all reading this to make plans, have that conversation, you know the one, because one day you'll be dead and your poor family who will mourn your passing don't want to be left worrying about finances, funerals, and what to do with the cat.

Of course, if you really don't like your family then just do nothing

This is the story of Alice (not her real name). Alice and her partner had been together for over forty years, they never felt the need to marry or put anything in place, well why would you, they were both in good health!

Yes, you've guessed it, cardiac arrest. Seventy-year-old male. We arrived to find Tom at the top of the stairs; he'd died where he had dropped, as instant as that.

Alice was sat on chair in the kitchen, just a stool in the middle of the floor, no expression on her face, we asked all the pertinent questions, have you any family, children etc?, no, Alice then went on to tell us, they weren't married, Tom looked after all the finances, they had no family at all, no brothers or sisters, they weren't friends with neighbours they kept themselves to themselves.

Alice didn't even know how much money they had, indeed anything about bank accounts, how to pay bills. She didn't even own the house.

We made the necessary arrangements, undertakers, GP etc, but I'll never forget the look on Alice's face as we left, just sat on the stool all alone.

We contacted social services for the possibility of some support, but it was so sad. I just wanted to take her home with me.

## Kinked Catheter

Sometimes it's the simple questions we forget. Take Alan (not his real name). Alan had recently had a catheter fitted and was still getting used to how to manage it. That day he became concerned because the catheter didn't appear to be working and as Alan's bladder started to fill, he became more and more uncomfortable, so he called for us to assist. Alan was sat on his settee, quite distressed, so after some questions and assessments from us we decided Alan should go to the hospital to get his blocked catheter fixed. So, Alan stood up to walk to the ambulance. It was at this point urine began to cascade from his open catheter. Note to self, check it's not just kinked. Red-faced, we returned to our ambulance, leaving Alan much relieved!

## After a night shift

Sitting like a zombie, conversation limited, apparently I'm a tad grumpy when I'm tired so imagine what the conversation is like when there are two of you who have just woken up after a night shift, to say the conversation is limited is an understatement, its mostly grunts, or one syllable words like 'no' all powers of communication have been left somewhere and decision-making has ceased to be viable, I have a theory that we actually leave our human selves in our lockers at work, I think in the future we will be plugging ourselves into charging points along with phones and computers. If someone shouted FIRE not having the energy to move, I'd probably just say, ya whatever, ring me when it gets hot!

The end of a night shift; not only is it the best feeling when your driving home, knowing that a nice cosy bed awaits and wild horses won't wake you but, that the cup of tea is also the best tasting? Your first day off after a night shift is also part of your sleep day. I've tried several approaches to the quandary of whether to stay up and get on with it or to go to bed and know your spending most of your day off in bed. The stay up approach has its drawbacks as by mid-afternoon I'm so tired I feel like I've had a stroke and can hardly speak so end up going to bed early. Then the go to bed theory straight away means you only sleep for 3–4 hours, waking feeling like you've been drugged. Oh, the joys!

## Buy one get one free birth

We sometimes get called to maternity emergencies but mostly it's a birth imminent and a midwife isn't available so we get sent to help. These have never been my favourite as too many things can go wrong. Over the years I've assisted delivering over ten babies, all successfully.

When baby decides to make an entrance there's not much you can do to stop it. We say things like "don't push, pant", and "cross your legs, we're nearly at the hospital".

On this occasion we'd got as far as outside a supermarket, pull over I shouted to the driver, "no don't push", too late! A healthy boy; mother and baby doing well, however I wasn't. As birth is a messy business, I was now wearing most of the amniotic fluid and blood.

I laughingly told the mother to put on the birth certificate, 'place of birth, supermarket, buy one get one free'.

## Cheek to cheek

I was working with a male colleague who had a bit of a reputation for being a ladies' man. We were called to a suspected stroke and the patient lived in a flat on the fourth floor. As it was necessary to take quite a lot of equipment with us, we decided to use the lift. The lift was the type that hasn't got a second guard door and was extremely small; with all of our kit and us it was a tight squeeze. Because there were no doors and just the wall, as the lift moved it was important to not touch the wall or the lift would automatically stop for safety.

We started to move up. I was leaning forward trying not to touch anything; however, my colleague was trying to take advantage and touch anything he could. I moved, trying to keep a safe distance, when the lift stopped between floors. A change of position was required but this was easier said than done and at one point we were cheek to cheek, much to his amusement. We were stuck in the lift for nearly twenty minutes before we found the reason for our sudden halt. A strap from our equipment had become lodged between the floor and the wall. Once this was rectified, we began to move again. When the doors opened, we just fell out of the lift in a heap. It must have looked very strange to the patients relative waiting for us, wondering why we were taking so long.

The patient hadn't had a stroke and was able to stay at home.

## Racism is alive and kicking

Diversity and equality is something drummed into us at the very start of our career in the NHS and quite rightly so; we work with many different communities so we need to be able to adapt accordingly and be respectful however, some of the general public don't have the same level of moral awareness and standards that we work to. Take Mrs Smith (not her real name).

We were called to a doctors' surgery; a patient was experiencing chest pains and the doctors weren't happy so they wanted her to have immediate blood tests in hospital.

We entered a side room where the patient and her daughter were sitting. We usually start with introductions but on this occasion we didn't get the chance as the patient on our entrance exclaimed "Thank god, it's two white women". I have to say I was somewhat taken aback but I kept going regardless. The patient's daughter apologised, explaining that mum had returned from South Africa because of ill health after living there for thirty years.

After the handover from the doctor we moved the patient to the ambulance where we continued with assessments and observations, the patient continued to say how glad she was to have white females taking care of her. It's at this point I couldn't stay silent any more.

The patient's daughter was with us on the ambulance so I advised the patient that her attitude and references to us was highly offensive and asked to not speak to us in this way anymore. I couldn't have made it any clearer. This was enforced by the daughter who also advised her mother that her views were not acceptable in this country.

It brought home to me just how far we have advanced in this country. I'm from a generation that grew up watching *The Black and White Minstrel Show* and *Love thy Neighbour* which wouldn't see the light of day now

When we entered the A&E department all the doctors on duty were Asian and male. I couldn't help myself. I turned to the patient and said, "It's not your lucky day" and left.

## An elderly colleague

During our working careers we are often placed to crew with other staff and on this occasion, I was working with a crew mate that was somewhat older than most of our esteemed colleagues. Needless to say, it was challenging at times but too much amusement.

We were called to assist a transport crew who were trying to take a patient with Parkinson's to a hospital appointment. The crew on scene needed to administer pain relief but also needed a helping hand and could not administer what the chap needed, we arrived to help, we took up our carry chair and Entonox and I administered the required drug to aid the chap's ability to move, we risk assessed the area and decided to use the carry chair to the stair lift, bring in the stretcher to the bottom of the stairs and had agreed a plan. However, my somewhat elderly crew mate who is rather hard of hearing got a little confused and a little tetchy! We got the chap to the stair lift but Joe (my crew) decided to assist by walking backwards, supporting the man to sit on the stair lift! As the stair lift was also behind Joe, he clumsily sat on the stair lift first, with the patient immediately on top of him! As we tried to correct the obvious mistake, Joe accidentally pressed the lever for the stair lift and they both started to career down the stairs on top of each other, sat firmly on the stair lift! The patient's wife could not believe her eyes as both parties shot down quicker than expected, with Joe moaning all of the way down because he had got his coat stuck under the patient's left bum cheek!

No one was injured during this fumbled procedure, except for my ribs from laughing. We managed to safely transfer the patient to the stretcher and he did get to his hospital appointment on time.

## Ghost on the Ward

During my nursing years we were often moved temporarily to other wards whilst a ward was being refurbished, during this period we were moved down in the basement into the old part of the hospital onto a Florence Nightingale ward whereby women were on one end and partitioned to the men on the other end.

It was a night shift and myself and a colleague were sat at the nurses' station updating records. It was 2 a.m.

and I happened to look down at the men's end and I saw a man stood right at the bottom of the ward at the end of a patient's bed. I nudged my colleague who flatly refused to go and check as he found these wards rather eery. I proceeded to go and investigate and had my torch to the ready. As I got nearer to the man he disappeared into the toilet, which only had that door as exit and entry! I checked every bed as I was heading in that direction and realised that every single patient was indeed in bed and asleep. I tried to alert my colleague, who froze to the spot and slowly entered the bathroom to which he had entered. I realised that it was empty? Nobody was in there.

As I left the bathroom, I checked the patient to where the man was stood and realised that the patient had passed away! Could the figure had been that very patient? Was he showing me he had gone? Needless to say, my colleague refused to work on that ward on a night shift again!

## Taser

Well some nights we are called to the very weird and wonderful, and this night in particular we were called to a young man who had decided, rather stupidly, to slit his wrists in protest to his uncle throwing him out! So, we were called to a house and we were confronted by a very aggressive soul who had blood oozing all over the floor and had decided to spray us (cheeky devil!) and to call us all of the names under the sun. He then went on to threaten his uncle with an extremely large baton whilst bleeding out. So, the boys in blue were called and when they arrived, the chap decided to then go completely batty on us. He was singing the theme tune to *Only Fools and Horses* and threatening the law, and us and his uncle!

By this time the chap was started to fade as he was losing blood and although we had dressed the wound, he was still not compliant. This was the point whereby the police decided to Taser him as we were all at great peril and he was waving his weapon around. We stood by from the ambulance when the man who was at this stage gently rocking back and forth but humming the theme music to *The Bill*, was tasered, it was like something from a *Police, Camera, Action* programme and every man was on him then. My crew mate at the time simply said "That must have stung!" and we all then were able to get on with our jobs and save him. Oh, the perils of youth!

Needless to say, the man survived and was rather tetchy on route to hospital, still managing to give us his middle finger and swear at the police who indeed accompanied us.

## She's a Biggun!

Daffers and I had been called to assist a man who had a urine infection and his son had called as his dad had started to eat less and urinate more. We arrived and entered the property and the son led us upstairs to the patient. I walked into the bedroom first, closely followed by Daffers. As Daffers stepped into the bedroom the man said in a very loud voice "Cor blimey, she's a big un!" On that Daffers looked rather disgruntled and immediately felt a wee bit self-conscious! I must add that Daffers is rather small so unless the patient was a little confused or was deliberately trying to goad her, who knows?

Anyway, after much discussion and assessments it was decided that the man needed to be taken to hospital and we asked the son to help us to get Dad onto his stair lift, which he did!

We proceeded downstairs and got the ambulance ready. When we returned into the property we saw the patient strapped into his stair lift and was slowly edging down the stairs. Unfortunately his son had placed him on the seat at an angle which made his head lean against the wall, as he came down further more and more friction was building up and his hair was getting higher and higher and the static build up was so much that by the time he arrived at the bottom he looked like 'Don King!' I had to leave the room as I could no longer hold my laughter which then set Daffers off.

Anyway, we then wheeled out the patient to the ambulance and had the task of getting the patient from the chair to the stretcher. The man was rather heavy and he was in no way cooperating, so we got an end each, I at one point had his ankles in a pincer movement and Daffers had the head end, he had soiled himself and Daffers' knee was helping to balance his bottom as he struggled against us, he did indeed at one point flip himself face first onto the stretcher but we managed to get him in a suitable position for transportation. Needless to say, it was a messy manoeuvre but we got him safely to hospital!

# Playground

Working in a hospital was an adventure. I was on an orthopaedic ward and it was a night shift. A lot of the patients were elderly and some had confusion. One night shift we were alerted by Security that there was an elderly patient on level 4 children's outside play area. Hearing this we quickly rushed to the toilet to see if Mr X was still on the throne as he was on there for some time regularly, so we had not thought anything to it! When we realised that he wasn't we immediately rang security who alerted us to look out of the level 5 window and low and behold there was Mr X swinging on the swings with his middle finger pointing up at us! Security gently escorted him back up where an exhausted Mr X requested sandwiches and tea before situating himself at the Nurses station to wait for the 59 bus home. He was a lovely eccentric old gentleman that kept us on our toes for the four weeks he was with us!

# Oh dear, she's only gone and trapped her hand!

It was a night shift and me and a colleague had been called to a forty-nine-year-old with central chest pain. The lady was of African origin and so with her medical history it was clear she was susceptible to cardiac issues. So, we arrived and after doing an ECG (heart tracing). It was clear that she was having an MI (heart attack). Once we had administered aspirin and GTN we called the cardiac unit for a bed and I was outside preparing the ambulance for transportation. At that point I heard an almighty yelp, followed by some very choice words and screaming that could make one's blood curdle. So, I had no option that to run inside to aid my colleague and find out what on earth was going on.

My colleague told me that as the lady was going to stand up, her daughter had slammed the lounge door and had trapped her hand in it, so we were probably also looking at a hand fracture. I could not contain my laughter as the lady was wailing at that point and the ridiculousness of the situation was too much. The lady was shouting in her native tongue and wailing and as I was laughing at my colleague's panic and I did not feel it appropriate to remain in the room and so I left her to deal with it.

What made my laughter escalate was seeing my extremely short colleague's head just about over the window sill mouthing obscenities to me because I had left her to deal with the situation Oh my, I was laughing so hard I think I actually peed a little that day.

## The Teenage Nun

We were driving back to base one October night shift, it was around 2 a.m. in the morning, it was cold and damp, we were tired and heading back for break when two security guards from a local university campus stood out near the road waving us down! At this point all we could see was a pair of stocking-clad legs, a nun and what looked like a 'slit throat!', anyway we grabbed our torches and investigated further into the bush and realised that this was a student who had been to a Halloween party and got bladdered, he had soiled himself and had a nun's outfit on and a fake slit throat. He could barely stand and was alone so we could not leave him there and decided to load him onto the ambulance and take him to hospital so that he could sober up with nursing staff to monitor him.

On the way, he persisted to vomit and soil himself every time he coughed, sneezed and vomited! The smell was horrendous, and even though I was my dutiful self, I had no other choice than to stand at the rear of the ambulance covering my nose! Daffers, seeing this in her rear view, found it rather amusing to go the long way to the hospital to make me suffer a little longer! I could see her shoulders frantically going up and down with laughter as she amused herself with her antics!

You should have seen the look of horror as we walked into A&E with a nun with a slit throat who had soiled himself! Needless to say, this young man was hosed down and made to sober up!

## The station Ghost

Myself and Daffers had just returned to the station having attended a cardiac arrest. We were alerted by a member of the public that one of our lights was out so returned to station to alert vehicle maintenance (VM) and replenish the vehicle. I waited outside station whilst Daffers made a cup of tea. We were waiting for a call from VM and they had my number and the station number, As I had missed a call from VM they tried ringing the station number at the same time I was trying to call them back.

As the station phone was ringing, Daffers ran from the kitchen to the office to answer the phone and as she was running down the corridor and stood outside in amazement, because as she was running there was a man running behind her. I was frantically pointing to her to look behind mouthing "who the hell is that?" She stopped and with an ashen look on her face, turned around. I had lost sight as she came to the front door but came out saying "What? What? There is nobody there?"

That night was very creepy, we were both reluctant to go back there for our break, there was an old station master that people believed haunted the station, often on a night we could hear doors closing with nobody else on. But we survived the night!

## We don't talk about religion

When you first join the service, we are warned that there are two subjects to avoid talking about and that's politics and religion, but sometimes it's unavoidable, such as when you're with a patient whose whole existence revolves around their belief and are adamant they're going to convert you.

Now, I can be naughty sometimes and take opportunities when they arise to play pranks on my crew mate Buntie. Feeling a little mischievous on this occasion I was talking to the patient who constantly directed the conversation back to her religion. So, knowing that Buntie would be with the patient in the back of our ambulance while we transported her to hospital, I told the patient that she was very interested and was sure she would benefit from hearing about the patient's views.

It took me nearly thirty minutes to drive to the hospital. When we arrived and I opened the rear doors to take the patient in I was greeted by what I can only described as 'a filthy look' from Buntie.

"How was your chat?" I asked.

"You wait," came the reply from Buntie.

## Nose Blind

The smell, it's not that bad is it?

We visit many care homes and the majority are really good. The residents or should I say 'service users' as they're supposed to be called are happy enough, their every need catered for however, some homes are not to these high standards.

When you walk into a property and the first thing you notice is the smell you must ask yourself why? I have no problem pointing this out to the staff who usually have an excuse waiting. 'Oh, it's one of the residents, they've got a UTI' (urinary tract infection), or something along those lines. Well, that doesn't wash with me, there simply is no excuse or all care homes would smell the same.

## Where do you live?

It was a summer's day. A lady had been found by a member of the public wandering in the park alone. She'd been walking around and around the park, which had alerted the member of public that something might be wrong.

When we arrived the lady in question was sat with a young man and his daughter. He explained that when he had asked the lady if she was OK, she had said she couldn't remember where she lived. We thanked the gentleman for his kind assistance and walked the lady to our ambulance.

This lady had no handbag or identification on her, she was unable to remember her address or home telephone number, and there was no evidence of injury, so it was a puzzle.

The lady looked about seventy-five years old, smart and clean. I sat chatting to her while my crew mate rang the police to see if anyone had reported a missing person.

The lady was wearing a large coat so asked if I could check her pockets. All she had was a leaflet from the local catholic church.

"Have you been to church recently?" I asked.

"Oh yes" she replied. "I go to church every Sunday; the nuns are lovely." The leaflet had a number on it. It was worth a try, just maybe they'll know her.

The nun who I spoke to thought she recognized my description; the church was only a mile away so I suggested that we drive over. As soon as the nun saw her, she knew who she was and better still, knew her address, husband's name and telephone number.

We called the husband who had been frantic with worry. "Don't worry, we'll bring her home." After tea and cake kindly given to us by the nuns, we returned the lady home. The story was that every day Mary (not her real name), would go for a walk in the park and return home after about an hour. Today she'd been gone nearly four hours. It turns out that Mary has dementia but nothing too serious that she ever got lost.

Today was a turning point for Mary, no more walks on her own. We suggested a talisman or similar just in case.

Mystery solved, no harm done, husband extremely grateful.

## Ninja

One evening we were alerted to a patient that was having a hypo (hypoglycaemic incident). We were told by his wife to go to the back gate as she could not open the front door. On arriving at the back gate we realised that we could not get in, as the gate was stiff!

Knowing that the patient was in urgent need of treatment I decided to use my ninja skills and kick the gate in! I took a running lunge kick and this fell flat as my leg ricocheted back sending me backwards!

Daffers then gently lent forward looking me in the eye and said "Maybe try the latch, Buntie!" and opened the gate! Did I feel a fool? Yes, I did! The patient recovered well! As soon as we got into the property, we administered lifesaving treatment. I still get leg pains from that kick though!

## I see dead people

We are often called to people who are having psychotic episodes. Who are suicidal or are having some sort of delusional hallucinations and as I write this, I do not wish that you think we trivialise such events. However, when you are there it can sometimes feel scary for us too.

We were called to a man who believed he was being attacked at home and had originally called for police assistance, however, the police did not attend so we were despatched. When we arrived at the property it was dark, there were no lights on and it was very quiet. We knocked on the door and waiting for at least fifteen minutes when a figure appeared, peering through the glass. He was shouting at us as he believed we had come to attack him! We assured him we were from the ambulance service and we were here to help.

He eventually let us in and he seemed very nervous; he was pacing and rocking, looking at the windows and doors and telling me that they were harassing him and he was scared. I sat on the floor and gently spoke to him. I reassured him that we would check the property and discuss options for him to access help. When suddenly he picked up his mobile phone as though he was talking to someone, the conversation he was having was very detailed and I asked if I could talk to whoever it was, he handed me his phone and it was off! So, it was clear that the man was having some sort of crisis and avenues were explored for his safety. Then all of a sudden he screamed with a bloodcurdling screech and jumped on the sofa ( I almost messed myself!). He said to us "Look, look can't you see them, they're the ghosts that come to take me and taunt me?" At this point we were getting nervous! I asked if he lived here alone and he said that his mum was in the bedroom next door! Myself and Daffers looked at each other, seriously expecting to find a corpse in the next room but luckily his mum was fast asleep oblivious to what was unfolding.

The man did get the help he needed from the available services that we have and we ensured both patient and his mum were OK before we left! I will never forget the fear in the man and us that night!

## I'm going to kill you both!

Sometimes in our line of work we are faced with scary and dangerous situations. We have been threatened and attacked and, in some cases, had to call for back up. In this story we had real fear for ourselves and those in the vicinity, as the patient was a real threat to us.

We were called to a man that was threatening suicide; he had been sectioned before and authorities were aware of him. We knew from the call details that there was a minimal threat but did not quite understand the seriousness of it until we stepped into his property.

It was a summer's afternoon and we got the call that a man had threatened to take his own life. We arrived and entered the property as the door was open and he did not answer but called us in. The man was in drink and was sat on his sofa just inside the door smoking a cigarette and watching TV.

I walked in first and asked if he minded me sitting on the sofa. Daffers stayed standing behind him. He fixated on me and started telling us that he had enough of living but wanted to end it. Daffers engaged and asked him what he intended to do. He stared at me and said that before he kills himself he was going to kill other people, then slowly declared without emotion that he was going to kill us two first! With that declaration, Daffers was looking at me, gesturing for me to stand up and get near to her! I, at that point, had lost control of my bowels and had gone weak at the knees with fear. I stood up, at which point he asked

"Why are you standing up?" I said I needed to stretch and my back hurt. Daffers distracted him by asking how he intended to do this, with her finger firmly on the panic button so that our control room could hear what was being said! At that point he reached under his legs and pulled out two machetes! He looked at me and said he intended to kill us both now and then kill people in the street. At that point I felt a hand firmly grab my collar and pull me outside! It was Daffers and he managed somehow to get outside.

Within what felt like seconds he had come outside and we felt a real threat to the public as a father and young daughter appeared next door. Luckily the police (armed) arrived and corned him and closed off the street, as Daffers wanted to jump out and shield the child, as did I. After police talked him down, we escorted him to hospital with police on board and he was supported by the Mental Health Team.

That day I think both myself and Daffers needed a clean pair of underwear!

## Ere Bob?

We were called out to a PV (per vagina) bleed to an elderly lady. Of course this can be serious in any lady who is post-menopause and this lady had gone through menopause almost thirty years ago!

Anyway, we arrived on scene and we were greeted by the patient's daughter and we were taken to the patient. On further discussion we had identified that the lady had called an ambulance the day before for the same problem and she explained that the two men ambulance crew did not look at the area causing her issues and said that she needed to speak to a doctor, however as she had continued to bleed, she had become rather concerned. So, we had to see what the problem was as we did not want to take a vulnerable lady to hospital with something that could be treated at home.

I appeared to have got the short straw as it was down to me to investigate with Daffers stood behind me holding a torch as the room was poorly lit! So, the patient volunteered to get on her bed and show me the offending area. Her daughter was at the end of the bed behind Daffers as we all waited with bated breath to see what was going on. It was very quickly clear that it was vaginal thrush and that she had scratched so hard that it was bleeding. As I explained to her what it was and the cream she needed her daughter declared that she had some of that and got on the phone to her husband to bring it over. We were privy to the phone call which went like this "Ere Bob, where's that cream I had for my fanny?" At which point both Daffers and I were chuckling and trying to be serious at the same time!

Bob did indeed bring the cream, at which point the patient said "I cannot reach me fanny! Can you please put it on otherwise I will still have an itchy foo!" We tried our hardest not to laugh. I donned two pairs of gloves and went in! As I got to the perineum the patient declared that she had just been for a poo! Charming! So, I quickly stood up and explained that she needed to sit comfortably now and apply more later herself!

Before we left, the patient was sat in her chair with her legs akimbo. We did stress that as her curtains were open that she needs to be careful who passes by for her own dignity, at which point the patient said "Oh that's

OK, love, the window cleaner will be coming soon anyway and may get more than he bargained for!"

We left and went onto our next call, thank goodness!

## The Night club Twat!

As often happens on a Saturday night, we get called to those savoury patients that are heavily drunk and annoying. This call was for a young lass who had collapsed inside a nightclub and she was part of a very large party that had travelled to Leicester from the North.

We arrive on scene and it was manic, busy and loud. We got the young lady on board with the help of bouncers and began our assessments of her. As we started it was very clear that the only issue was that she was drunk and was wearing very little clothing. She was beginning to get mouthy with us and so we were trying to complete the assessment when someone was banging on the ambulance doors. This continued for about twenty minutes and using our security camera we could see that it was a young man who was part of her party.

Daffers was getting a little cheesed off and went outside to explain that we were assessing his friend and to be patient. So, getting back in the ambulance, Daffers and I continued supporting the patient when the chap started to bang the ambulance doors again, at which point Daffers jumped outside waving her ninja finger and said "Now look here, you twat! Stop banging the door, this is an ambulance not a front door!" She was just trying to get the young man to be respectful and we were caring for the girl so it was inappropriate to knock continuously

Needless to say, the young man retreated under the nearest rock and stopped his banging! Well done, Daffers!


# The Prison

When we get a call to a prison its usually a serious job, so on this occasion we realised that we were going to a bad job when it came through as 'man slit throat and bleeding heavily', so we dashed there like the clappers and when we arrived the prison doors were already open with guards waving us through! At that point we knew it was bad, because it usually takes at least thirty minutes to get through security and be slowly walked around.

We got to the medical wing and guards were running out, helping us with kit. We ran upstairs to the patient and there was blood! Lots of it all over the floor. The patient had indeed slit his throat from ear to ear, there was a nurse holding his head forward to stem the bleeding but all of their staff were panicking and relieved to see us. We quickly went into the cell trying to get access to a vein but because he had lost so much blood and his blood pressure was so low it was impossible. I radioed for Air Ambulance who carry doctors and within minutes they had landed. Daffers and I were sliding around in the blood trying to gain clinical observations when I had bent down near his feet and Daffers was at his head. I went to stand up at one point and my head nearly got lost up Daffers' rear end.

We remained calm and when Air Ambulance arrived, we worked as a team to get access and transport him by road to the nearest trauma centre. It was very rushed but he survived! Well done all of us!

## Falling for my patient

We were called to a care home for patients that were non-English speaking. The care staff let us in and took us to a room of an elderly patient that she believed had stroked! When we got there, I started to unload and attach my kit to get assessments in place. The patient did not understand so the carer translated. At this point Daffers had sat on a chair behind me to do our electronic paperwork and the carer was stood the opposite side of the bad. I had my blood pressure cuff and lent over the bed to get her arm, I started to feel a little off balance and as I leant over, I toppled directly on top of the patient and face planted a somewhat savoury armpit! The carer had forgotten to put the brakes on the bed! At that point as my legs and bottom were in the air Daffers exclaimed "Oh dear, I put cellulite on mine!" Cheeky mare!

We took the patient in and all of the way in she was staring at me with an expression of fear! The patient was fine.

## One of her legs

Occasionally when we hand over at hospital, we are greeted with a bunch of somewhat miserable HALOs (Hospital Ambulance Liaison Officer) and nurses. I have never understood why as we should be working as a team. Anyway, we had walked into the ambulance assessment area and was greeted by a HALO. She clearly did not get our sense of humour and had a face like a bag of smashed crabs! When handing over, Daffers told her that the patient has had a previous DVT (deep vein thrombosis). The HALO looked bewildered and said "Where?" So Daffers looking somewhat shocked said in a very bemused fashion "In one of her legs!" Atat this point I could not stop laughing as the HALO then said "What is she laughing at? I meant to say when, not where!" so we were then pushed to the back of the queue for being too jovial. I guess you needed to be there but it was the way the HALO asked and how Daffers answered it that tickled me.

## Motorway Jumpers

Some jobs just send shivers down the spine. It was a sunny Saturday dinner time and I was working with a male crew that had been on the service for many years. We were just clear at a job and a call came through for two jumpers on the motorway. I instinctively thought it was a pair of teenagers and so drove like the wind to get there. We got a call en route that said the two had jumped straight into the fast lane so we knew this was going to be bad.

After fighting with traffic to get through we arrived. The motorway had come to a standstill. Cars were tooting and people were wandering on the motorway to have a look. Fire crews and police were there and Air Ambulance doctors were on their way. If I could describe how it felt then it would be like time had frozen and it was surreal. There were two elderly people on the motorway; one was clearly dead as their body was contorted and brain matter everywhere, the other was still twitching. I ran with my defibrillator and cut the person's clothes open so I would check his injuries and apply the shock pads. There was an off-duty nurse holding his head for me and we attempted to get an airway in but he was in trismus. I assessed for rhythm and bizarrely enough he was still beating but very seriously ill. We applied a pelvic binder and all around me felt like mayhem and yet I felt alone. Within minutes Air Ambulance doctors arrived, firefighters closed the opposite side of the motorway and they got to him. They asked me to assist in swapping our equipment to their ZOLLS (an earlier defibrillator model), and they had RSI'd (rapid sequence intubation) him within seconds. We assisted them to get the patient onto their helicopter so he could get to the trauma centre.

Meanwhile fire crews had covered the deceased body over and SOCO arrived, taking pictures. I met up with my crew mate and incident control COMs (manager), and had a debrief before returning to base to restock and have a TRIM (trauma risk management) meeting, which is to assess how well you have coped. Within an hour we were back on the road to our next patient. It was something that I will never forget and I can still see those images very clearly, but it is what we do!

# This was not just a faint!

Every now and again we are called to jobs that strike a chord. This particular one affected myself and Daffers very much and we still think and talk about it eighteen months on. The job had come through as a faint so we did not expect to see what we did when we reached the job.

We were greeted at the door by a family member who looked very distressed. She pointed for us to go upstairs and as we turned the corner, we saw a young man, naked, his skin was hanging off him and he had soiled himself. He was cradled by his wife who was distraught. We didn't even look at each other but knew instinctively that what we were dealing with happened to be a life or death situation.

We started to assess him and his initial readings were dire, saturating at below 40 percent oxygen. We knew that he needed to be treated in hospital and aside from the clinical interventions we had to support and be empathetic with the family, so we involved them in every move, every decision and ensured that it was swift but gentle. Daffers ran outside to bring in the carry chair as we needed to get him downstairs and onto the ambulance. We had his father and son helping to carry him but we had stressed that as soon as we moved him he was likely to go into cardiac arrest. His blood pressure was so low but had no venal access so we just needed to move, and move quickly!

As we got him onto the carry chair his arms started to raise and he went into cardiac arrest. We were shouting to get downstairs quickly so that we could attempt CPR (chest compressions). We got him onto the kitchen floor and applied pads, however they were slipping off because his skin was dropping off, so we inserted the airway and begin saving him. Every step of the way we explained what we doing to the family, who were terribly anxious and distraught as he was a very young man who had a form of cancer.

Daffers had to move the ambulance nearer and we had done ten minutes of CPR and managed to get him onto the ambulance where his wife remained in the back and helped with Daffers. I drove and had his son in the front with me. All I could focus on was getting him to hospital and drove like the wind. When we arrived at Accident and Emergency the look of horror from staff as we barged in through the doors was apparent on all of their faces.

We got him there alive but unfortunately he passed away around thirty minutes later. The reason this job was very poignant was because I was going through a situation similar to this at home but also, we are both mothers and to see his wife, mother and children so upset and so distressed it really hit home! This job was much more than a faint and it will be a job that we both remember until we say goodbye to the world. It was emotionally, clinically and physically demanding but we can only take from this that we supported the family, involved them and got him to hospital alive.


## Cluttered house v Defibrillator

I'm a clumsy so and so sometimes! I had visited a patient who was not feeling well and she had a very cluttered house. We had finished our assessments and it was clear that she was anxious and not having a heart attack! So, I tidied up my equipment, stood tall and turned around. As I did, I cleared her shelf full of collectable frogs and they smashed around my ankles! Oops! At this point the patient began having another panic attack and I was there for another hour. I offered to pay for the damage but when she came through her attack, she declared that she never really liked the frogs as they belonged to her ex-partner and thanked me! Needless to say, she ended up laughing and I am more careful in cluttered properties! Haha!


## I just sat on the floor

Occasionally we have our patience tested by the public, especially those that think it is OK to call for an Emergency Ambulance because they have watched a programme on TV. This was one of those occasions. We got the call that a lady had fallen and could not get up, we arrived and went in as she had left the door on the latch.

We noticed she was watching *999: What's Your Emergency?* and she had managed to 'fall' onto the carpet from the sofa! Not!

I was a little cheesed off and asked her if she could get onto her knees, she did. I then asked her if she could lean on the sofa with her elbows, she did! I then asked her to pull herself up onto the sofa, she did! She had now got herself up and as she sat there asked us to change her clocks an hour as she had not done it yet and the clocks went back yesterday!

This was a forty-five-year-old lady who had not fallen but had watched TV and thought it might be fun to get the ambulance service in her home! Unbelievable!

# Heavy patient vs Hoist

Working on a hospital ward sometimes has its own hazards, especially when a rather large lady needs to be hoisted onto a commode chair. It was a busy day and visitors had come to the ward, the lady's husband had arrived but she needed a poo first, so we closed the curtains and I had asked one of the nursing assistants to get the hoist. The commode chair was in place and all straps were ready from the hoist. I was one side of the bed and the NA (nursing assistant) was the other and had the controls, so she started to raise the patient and knowing the husband was the other side of the curtain we made sure that we verbalised the procedure, except when the hoist began to topple with the weight of the patient and my exact words were " oh shit, we need to lower her!" At that point the hoist toppled with me underneath the patient. The NA was laughing, the patient was screaming and I had my face firmly squashed into her bed sheets which were smeared with poo! It was struggling to stand up and help needed to be called! We could hear the patient's husband asking what the hell was going on?

Anyway, after about twenty minutes, assistance from other staff and the lady's husband she managed to use facilities, have her sheets changed and welcome her visitor in style!

I on the other hand was able to wash my face but the smell of her poo was stuck up my nostrils for the rest of the shift! The moral of the story is to check the weight capacity of equipment before you attempt a move!

# False teeth and wigs

On hospital wards when a patient dies, we lay them out, call relatives to say their goodbyes, we wash and tidy the patient and collect belongings. Once the relatives have been, we inform the porters to take the deceased to the mortuary. Sometimes things do not go to plan!

We had an elderly lady pass away on a night shift; it was expected but her son and daughter had told us to call them at any time so they could say goodbye to Mum. The relatives arrived earlier than anticipated and we were behind the curtains combing Mum's hair, making the bed tidy and on this occasion placing her false teeth back in her mouth so she looked more like herself.

Things started to go wrong as rigor mortis was starting to develop and so placing her false teeth in was becoming rather tricky! Every time I put them in, they dropped down! At one point she looked a cross between Sefton and Janet Street-Porter! Her wig would not sit correctly and kept lifting and at that point I got a fit of the giggles! Knowing the relatives were the other side of the curtain I tried my hardest to muffle my laughter so much so I peed myself. The relatives thought we were crying because my colleague also developed the giggles! The poor woman looked like a shocked vampire by the time we finished and when the relatives came in to see her they said how lovely she looked, which made me choke on my laughter., I had to cover my face and run off, apparently they said to my colleague that if I need a hug to come back to them! Needless to say, I kept well away until the porters arrived!

I do apologise but sometimes when we know we should not laugh it becomes harder to control ourselves.

## The coronavirus! (Buntie)

Well, what a year! Never have I ever known a virus to bring the world to a standstill. When we found out about world events we were scared beyond belief; we used to sit in the ambulance trying to work out how the world could ever recover. We mulled over ideas of conspiracy theories, looked at what happened with the virus, cried over claps on a Thursday night and watch figures unfold. It was a time of shops allowing us food and drinks, community spirit and clapping every Thursday night. We noticed a drop in calls initially because people did not want to go to the hospital. We were trained in respirator wearing and had to get used to wearing space suits. It will go down as part of history but the fear we felt initially will remain.

## When to call the Fire Service

We sometimes get called to patients that have not been seen for days and neighbours start to worry. On this particular occasion we were greeted after returning on station by a neighbour of a lady who had not been seen. In fact, she had not come out on the Thursday night to clap for the NHS and did so religiously!

So, we drove over and attempted to attract the lady's attention. We went round the back of the house and banged so loud that other people in the street had come outside to see what the commotion was. After thirty minutes of trying we knew we had to radio control who then alerted the fire service who are actually stationed next door.

Fifteen minutes later the fire crew showed up with their big red key. After realising there was no other way in they began to remove the glass and bang their way in (resulting in the door being a right off!). We walked into the property and there was a dreadful smell, so we were preparing for the worst. But the patient had simply felt poorly, took her hearing aids out and gone to bed. When we woke her up, she just said "Oh, hello!" and proceeded to pull the duvet over her head and fall back to sleep!

Needless to say, the neighbour arranged a locksmith/door repair and stayed with her until the property was secure! Thank you, fire service.

## Police should knock

We had been called to an RTC and had our patient on board, he had driven into a ditch so was on our stretcher in head blocks, on a scoop and was basically boarded and collared!, for the head blocks there is a strap that should firm the head and as I was not looking where I had strapped this contraption the strip slipped down over his eyes making him look like a cyborg! Anyway, we were assessing the patient and so we had to strip him down to expose and assess him, when all of a sudden a police officer had opened the back door and started to ask the patient questions! It clearly says on the back of an ambulance to knock first! Well, Daffers lost her shit! She said "Now, young man, look here! In future you will knock on the door before entering an ambulance! We must consider the dignity of our patients!" A very sheepish police officer slowly retreated from our ambulance with his eyes to the floor.

And Daffers did not leave it there! With her ninja finger loaded she went outside and told the young officer off while I carried on assessing the patient! Needless to say, that officer of the law will knock before he enters in future!

## Roland Rat and the limp

We were driving to base when we got a call out to a man limping in the town and knocking on doors, claiming he had been in a car accident. We drove to the destination that our control room had sent us, when we saw a young man wearing a hood and limping. He was waving us down so we pulled over. I asked him if he was OK and was it him that called for an ambulance? He confirmed and jumped on board but was in a manic state and tried to explain that he was at a party when a friend called to say he had been in an RTC so he was looking for him. He said that he had twisted his knee and borrowed crutches from a good Samaritan.

OK, so we assessed him and to do this I needed him to take his trousers down so I could see his leg. At that point, maybe due to embarrassment, he started to laugh 'like Roland Rat!' Well that just set Daffers off laughing, so she retreated to the driver's seat. He was clinically OK and nothing was broken but he told us that he had no means to get home. We radioed control and explained that we would take the patient home as we have a duty of care to him and on the way Daffers had noticed that there had indeed been an RTC and a police car was in attendance. So we began our detective work, put two and two together and pulled alongside the police officer. Daffers asked him how a car had managed to land on top of another car in a car park and he explained that two young men were seen limping away from the accident and one had been arrested. Daffers explained that we may indeed have someone on board that he may wish to talk to and explained what he had told us. The police officer jumped in the back to talk and we heard the sounds of Roland Rat laughing and then the officer get off!

We were stunned that the officer did not take this any further and could not put two and two together! So, Roland got lucky that day as we took him home to Mummy!


## Mary's baps

We had been called to a patient and his wife was making us a cup of tea and then kindly offered to make us bacon baps, which is a very rare event as we can go all day without a break. Anyway when she offered this, we snapped it up and sat to chat with her. We were talking to her and her sons when she said that she did not like my tattoos, and also did not like her son having a tattoo. I am very respectful that people have their own views on tattoos and you either love them or hate them, but I asked her if there was anything I could say or do to make her change her mind? In fact I even offered to have my next tattoo devoted to her, however I did not think before I spoke and bearing in mind she had made us bacon baps I proudly (and in front of her family) declared that I was going to have my next tattoo of "Mary's Baps!" The look of horror on Mary's face said it all! Needless to say, we swiftly left the property trying to apologise and explain that I did not mean to be disrespectful.

## Grandma Seizure

Some patients and their relatives do not fully understand what they mean when they talk about their conditions, usually to the amusement of myself and Daffers. We had gone to a patient that had felt odd and her family greeted us at the door. It was a cluttered house; children were all over the place and animals in the garden. The patient sat on the sofa and was of a large build but sat wearing nothing more than a skimpy t-shirt and flashing her undercarriage.

Anyway, the patient was still a little dazed but clinically stable, so her daughter started to tell us what Mum suffered with. She had gone down a very long list when she told us that mum was epileptic and had "Grandma Seizures!" I could not stop laughing and had to leave the room with the excuse that I needed to get something from the ambulance. Poor Daffers had to continue alone with the family shouting out Mum's ailments from fanny rash to a Veronica on her foot from swimming! Oh, the joys of the English Language.

## Playing tricks on your crew mate

Daffers and I play tricks on each other. I am not sure how or we it started but I have a history of being somewhat mischievous and so has she. In the past I have played tricks on people such as packing cardboard sandwiches for their dinner, sewing the sleeves of an ex-partner's coat and so on.

So far Daffers has pushed me onto a urine-soaked bed, shaken a wet tree branch over my head as I was getting out of the ambulance and banged the stretcher as I was reversing to make me think I had crashed. I have jumped out on her from behind the ambulance, leapt out in her car window as she sat playing solitaire on her phone and stuck a label on her coat saying "kick me!".

We are level at the moment but no doubt we will continue to get the better of each other!

## Sound advice to a student!

Sometimes we have students on board with us. This particular student was a lovely young man and we had noticed how respectful he was with the patients; this is a must in the health sector and so we were very happy for him to take the lead on this assessment. We had gone to a lady who was somewhat confused, we had assessed her and decided that she needed further assessments at the hospital. As we were packing up our kit and helping her to get some bits together, she grabbed the student's hand and slowly looked into his eyes saying "The best advice I can ever give you is "ssssssss! Well I am sure our student will take that advice to the grave! Whether she was speaking parcel tongue or was just a little off that day, one will never know but it was amusing and lovely to see our student accept this advice graciously.

# The elephant in the room

Action, consequence? Let just say it like it is, for god's sake, let's stop pussyfooting around the subject.

Some doctors are awful at just saying what needs saying, delivering information that they know the patient won't like, they wrap it up in medical speak, the poor patient has no idea or concept of what they are saying, when really the medical profession is saying, bloody well take responsibility for yourself, engage with us, we can help you, you constantly push us away so what the hell do you want us to do?

So, what is the answer? You see it's simple: for some patients if they were to engage then the game, their game, would be over! Harsh words, I hear you say.

And it is a game I'm afraid one that is played out countless times by people who quite frankly enjoy it (unknowingly,) it keeps them away from responsibility, away from the rigors of daily life, it's the truth, for example and there are many but ill narrow it down to just one!

Meet Mary (not her real name). She had a chronic condition which gave her a lot of pain. I'd met Mary before several months earlier she was challenging then and today she was much more challenging as she had gone through the system many times, seeing one specialist after another, learning as she went what to say and how to get a reaction. I felt for her and wondered what I could do to help.

I was working with Lucy. It was decided as the patient was on a shedload of medication all of which had a sedentary effect, we had to be careful what we gave her for her pain, if anything!

The patient was clearly in distress. My crewmate made the call to the patient's surgery the information that came back was enlightening: numerous visits to the GP, numerous visits to hospital, numerous cancelled appointments with health care professionals – a pattern was beginning to emerge.

When we told the patient we'd spoken to the doctors at the surgery she went nuts. It was like we'd found her dirty secret.

'You don't believe me!' she shouted. 'You're like all the rest, no one wants to help me, you're being cruel.' What the? I was gobsmacked. My crew mate was really upset at being called cruel when we had worked so hard to help.

We were in the ambulance, I had a captured audience, and I was very upset with how we'd been spoken to, the patient had been demanding and manipulative, the husband now onboard the ambulance, clearly exhausted by it all.

'Let's talk about the elephant in the room,' I said.

"No, no, I don't want to,' cried the patient.

'Well, tough, here it comes', I said.

'Oh, thank god,' said her husband.

"How's your mental health?"

"I'm seeing a psychiatrist." Bingo!

"At last someone who understands and gets it," the husband exclaimed.

So, the pattern was not getting her own way. She'd accuse everyone, shout, scream, make everyone's life a living hell including her family, who were at the end of their tether, children threatening and desperately wanting to leave, her husband on his knees emotionally, still this 'learnt' behaviour carries on. I say learnt because over the years patients come to learn that any attention, be it negative or otherwise, is some attention and its as basic as that, some of the population of people who without realising it feel unloved, worthless, a burden and crave whatever attention they can get.

Now, let's not forget, this patient was in pain, a chronic condition which could be managed but nonetheless still painful and this continued to be our area of focus but I don't think I was one of her favourites.

## Do you mind, I'm eating?

Sometimes, the ambulance and police force join forces and work together, this was one of those occasions, a police officer and a paramedic in an ambulance car posted in the city centre, it was a Saturday night the pubs and clubs were beginning to fill. There were various misdemeanours happening; men urinating in public, rowdy drunk revellers and fights breaking out here and there.

The police woman, Jodie (not her real name), that I was working with got a call on her radio – fight in McDonald's – off we set. It was literally a minute away, around the corner from where we were waiting. I was driving. I pulled up outside the restaurant and sure enough it was kicking off big time, a couple of lads were going at it, fist flying, lots of shouting, quick as a flash, Jodie jumped out and dashed into the restaurant, she didn't hesitate, I was impressed! There was much flaying of arms and more shouting from Jodie as she battled to get things under control, I kept a safe distance outside! well, there was nothing I could do, as this wasn't my remit. I'd wait to see if anyone needed treatment.

Next thing I knew, the pepper spray was being used liberally. That did the trick, unfortunately not only did it stop the lads in their tracks it also got the security guard and anyone else close enough. I distinctly remember hearing a customer shout, "Do you mind, Officer, I'm trying to eat my burger?"

## Where is the body?

Called to a cardiac arrest, I arrived on my own, police where on scene, OK so, what do we have, 'a female dead in her flat, OK let's have a look, I entered a flat that was heaving with stuff, clothes, food, waste, furniture and mattresses, OK so.

"Where's the body?" I asked.

"Up there," a policeman said.

"Up where?" I followed his directions and gaze. Oh my god, in front of me was a bed stacked with mattresses. I counted about twenty until I couldn't see any more. "You're kidding me, surely she's not on top of all those."

"Yes," came the reply.

I climbed up very slowly, expecting to fall at any moment. When I reached the top, sure enough there she was. God bless her, she'd passed away all alone amidst her worldly possessions. Who knows why she lived the way she did but I didn't get the feeling she had been a bad person. RIP.

# It's not funny

Middle of winter we'd had a snow storm over night and as it was the weekend lots of people had taken the opportunity to find a hill somewhere and slide down it on all sorts of equipment, dustbin lids, plastic bags etc. A call came in: male, suspected broken leg at a well-known beauty spot and hill.

When we arrived, it was still daylight and the temperature had remained below freezing all day. I gingerly stepped out of the ambulance and immediately fell straight onto my back. The place was packed with mums, dads and kids and loads of teenagers. As much as I tried to stand up I simple slide straight back down. I was like Bambi on ice. My efforts were causing much amusement to everyone watching. I eventually gave up on standing and crawled to the edge of the hill. My crew mate was having similar difficulties.

The patient was halfway down the hill. He was in his early twenties and he and his mates thought it would be a good idea to use an old armchair to ride on down the hill. He'd come off at the first bump and landed awkwardly on his leg and now couldn't move.

We needed to get to him somehow so, with as much kit as we could manage, we started to descend. It's at this point momentum and the weight of our kit took over. My crew mate and I went hurtling past the patient and landed at the bottom of the hill.

Luckily, a special team had been asked to attend given the weather condition, they arrived just in time to see us crawling back up the hill for the umpteenth time.

The patient was rescued successfully and so were we.

# The dog under the kitchen table

Well, we often go into a patient's house and are confronted by many types of creatures, dogs, cats, birds, snakes and all have their own relevant affection to the patient. This particular day we were called to a lady who had fallen in the kitchen. She lived with her sister and her dog named Teddy.

So, we have assessed and raised the patient from her kitchen floor and ensured she was well. The lady was not for transport.

During the mayhem of making sure the lady was safe we realised we had left open the back door and gate. The patient's sister started to panic as they were sure Teddy had escaped, so Daffers went with the patient's sister who was a jolly eccentric! And I could hear them both shouting "Teddy, Teddy!" as I was reassuring the patient that Teddy would be fine.

So, ten minutes later and still searching I decided to help with the search, we knew Teddy was hard of hearing so I decided to bang on the floor as I believed that vibration may alert him rather than shouting. It was at that point that I knelt on the floor near the dining room table and noticed a paw, so I climbed under the table but not near enough to get bitten! I banged on the floor and continued to shout his name, doing the obligatory kissing sound. It was then that I realised Teddy was in fact dead! So, I swiftly jumped up and never declared that Teddy was indeed dead underneath the dining table! I think they had enough excitement and stress that day and did not want to impose on what would inevitably be a sad and emotional experience.

Note to the wise, if visiting people with pets, always close the garden gate, never get on your hands and knees and try to understand that pets are family members!

## How we lived through the coronavirus (Daffers)

It's Saturday March 28th 2020, I can't even remember when all this started. I work with my regular crew mate Marie AKA Buntie, it seems we have all slipped into this endless routine of woe, the daily grind of helping the population come to terms with this invisible enemy which is very successfully killing us off at an alarming rate, the virus that culled the human race. Mother Nature getting her revenge!

It's just been announced that our own prime minister (Boris Johnson) has the virus. This virus doesn't discriminate; the heir to the throne Charles has it, these are people who meet people, shake many hands just like us so, how long before we get it?

Well, we're tough in the ambulance service and just get on with it regardless. We accept the inevitable but plough on anyway. You don't join a caring service like ours to run away at the first sign of trouble.

On Thursday March 26th at 8 p.m. there was an outpouring of love and support from the public the likes of which I have never seen. Everyone from monarchs and prime ministers to shop keepers and neighbours, they all stood in the street and clapped, clapped to say thank you to all of the NHS workers, all the people still able to go to work to help our country get through this. It was such an emotional moment and I'm crying while I write this. Our ambulance was HIT, not in an aggressive way, if you were 'hit' it meant someone had left you food, chocolates, coffee, the modern reusing of a word that would normally mean something bad, like bad means good in kids' speak! So, we'd been 'hit', chocolates accompanied by cheers and clapping. Wow!

Our colleagues were falling by the wayside, having to self-isolate, so the staff numbers were dropping rapidly. The remaining were having to take up the slack but there's only so much you can do and, in our job, you must look after number one.

Due to the 'stay at home' policy that had now been enforced, seeing family was out of the question, FaceTime, Skype, Alexa all came into their own but, these too were showing signs of strain. It was hard to not be able to visit and have precious cuddles from the grandkids; how we've taken these things for granted.

So, at this moment in time, the garden looks great, all those jobs we've put off are finally getting done as quite frankly if you're not working there's nothing else to do! I predict that there will be a baby boom in nine months' time, plus a whole load of divorces. Someone always makes money out of a crisis.

Patient has left white blood cells at another hospital.

She has no rigors or shaking chills, but her husband states she was very hot in bed last night.

On the second day the knee was better, on the third day it disappeared.

The patient was tearful and crying; she also appeared depressed.

Patient had waffles for breakfast and anorexia for lunch.

The patient has been depressed since she began seeing me in 1993.

While in A&E, she was examined, X-rated and sent home.

The patient was present when suppository was inserted.

Alert with episodes of forgetfulness.

Patient has history of 'Pickle cell Anaemia'.

Vaginal packing out, Dr Lee in.

Bleeding began in the rectal area and continued all the way to Los Angeles.

Surgery will be performed under general Anastasia.

The pelvic examination will be done later on the floor.

Skin somewhat pale but present.

Large brown stool ambulating in the hall.

Patient has two teenagers, but no other abnormalities.

The patient refused an autopsy.

She is numb from the toes down.

Exam of genitalia reveals that he's circus-sized.

The patient was prepped and raped in the usual manner.

Both breasts are equal and reactive to light and accommodation.

Suppositories given, sat on toilet with no results, will try again after Christmas.

Social history reveals this 1-year-old does not smoke, drink and is presently unemployed.

Patient's foot was amputated above the knee.

Following the examination of her breasts we discussed the impending nasal surgery.

His progress was poor, having a massive cerebral haemorrhoid.

Rectal exam reveals normal-size thyroid.

Both her old and new noses have been placed in our album.

# Conclusion

Thank you for reading our book. We hope that you have been able to take the humour from our adventures. We just wanted to allow an insight into the world of the Green Army. We do take our jobs and the patients extremely seriously but please understand that we need humour in order to survive and in no way are we mocking anyone. We love people and we love to cheer them up. We are two women of a certain age with masses of life experience behind us and we use this in our day-to-day job.

Enjoy our stories, enjoy our humour and if you would like to keep up to date with us, we are on Facebook and the local radio. Search 'Buntie Daffers'. You can also book us for 'An Audience with Buntie and Daffers' for after-dinner speakers etc, via Call Us Events website or C.U.E. for short.

Look out for our children's series of books *The Adventures of the Ambulance Family.*